A Treasury of American Song

A TREASURY OF

American Song

BY OLIN DOWNES AND
ELIE SIEGMEISTER

HOWELL, SOSKIN & CO.

NEW YORK

The Contents

Introduction

THE SONGS in this Treasury have been sung by the generations and kinds of people who have made America. They have been selected from an overwhelmingly rich store of material with a view to providing informal entertainment. But there is more than that in the matter. If ever there was a time in the history of our nation that our people should know themselves and renew faith in the purposes and traditions which are part of us, that time is now. This faith and these accretions of national experience are expressed in the most characteristic of our songs. They come directly and without intellectual corruption from the people, of whom Lincoln said so tenderly that God must have loved them since he made so many of them. Some of their songs are serious and some comical; some carry the ache of a beloved memory, others fairly quiver with the strength and exultation of a confident youth; or they are flippant, waggish, sentimental; they caper to the rhythms of honky-tonks or the nervous pace of city street; and some have the cosmic beat of seas and tides, and properly pertain to the culture which produced a Melville and a Whitman. All of them, come from far or near, from yesterday or immemorial ages behind us, are part of the American adventure and the great sweep of the national epic.

These songs are not *belles lettres,* and they do not represent the classical education. Yet they tell more of certain fundamental things, than many histories or political or sociological disquisitions. The song begins where the event stopped. It is the essence of life, feeling and action. One consults the written record for facts which can or cannot be made to speak the heart of a community or epoch. The songs *are* the heart of the men and the epoch and as such constitute the most eloquent and humanly revealing of all our records. Whitman, who craved a form of art which should have their naturalness, said that he would allow no methods or sophistications to come between him and the truth, and that he would seek in his poems the unimpeachable and careless rectitude of the plants and the animals. Such rectitude may be discovered in many of our people's melodies.

One extraordinary fallacy sustained through long years in circles that should have known better, can readily be scouted by the contents of this volume. It has been said by pedantic or snobbish persons that America has no native songs of her own. America is overflowing with native songs and has sung them through every stage of her evolution and is constantly creating new ones. One reason for these erroneous conclusions lay in the superficial estimates of the nation's musical lore which have been made in allegedly cultivated circles. Thus it has been said that the only American folk songs are those of the Indians, or the contributions of the American Negro; that the remainder of our native music consisted of popular dance tunes and folk music imported from Europe. Do these critics really believe that the folk music of any nation is the simon pure product of its soil? Or of a single period? Folk music is created everywhere and its seeds are flung on the winds to uncounted destinations. If the seed is strong and falls on propitious soil, it flourishes. Under other conditions it perishes. If it thrives, it seldom fails eventually to cross with another neighboring species. In no country have there been so many cross-fertilizations as in America, and in no country have these cross-fertilizations given more strength, variety and vigor to the native product.

Hence the arrangement of the songs in this

volume in a sort of rough, geographical and historical sequence, but in ways more indicative of their character and mood than of the place or date—usually unknown—of their composition. Any other design would have been difficult and out of keeping with the vastness of the theme and the delightful conglomeration of the subjects. If this were a collection of folk airs of some older country and more settled civilizations, a more precise method might have been followed. But there are no more hard and fast classifications of the songs of the American people than there has been regularity in the development of our society or consistency in the program of our education.

It is not too much to say that the literature of American popular song is indeed a literature of unparalleled democracy, not only in the matter of it, but in the manner of its assimilation and recreation by the people.

We need not claim that these processes of growth and metabolism and multiplication are unique with us. The popular music of all nations is a composite. But the place held by this music in the consciousness of older nations seems both culturally and socially to have been stratified. It may have been music of common knowledge, but it was not music of common experience. A landowner, let us say, had peasants whose dancing and singing he loved. They sang to him and he always cherished the melodies. No doubt the songs were embedded in his affections; no doubt they kept warm his memories of his homeland when he was far away. But he never knew what it was to sing side by side with the peasant or improvise melodies while he hauled a barge on a river or reaped the harvest.

In America the great majority of its citizens, especially in the first two centuries of the nation, worked with their hands, wandered the country, shared on unequivocal terms the common lot, the common tasks and vicissitudes. True, there did develop the gentleman landowner, especially in the period of slavery in the South. But in the mass and as a whole there were not the old barriers, either of cus-

tom or culture, to divide the people; and that community of thought is reflected in the songs and their manner of singing by every type of citizen and every sort of people.

And how strangely these currents and eddies of popular culture rushed and swirled. They were primarily consequent, of course, upon the movements of the population. Thus a group, principally of Scotch-Irish, comes a little belatedly to the South, when the best plantation lands have been pre-empted. But the Western frontier is advancing by leaps and bounds and there are stories of marvelously rich land in the direction of the sunset. So this group turns West, gets caught in the hills of Kentucky and Tennessee, and is almost segregated for more than a century from the rest of the people of the continent. They, therefore, preserve, with a fidelity to tradition which astonished the English folk-lorist, Cecil Sharpe, when he visited the district some dozen years ago, a large number of old British folk songs in their pristine purity, of which the original forms had vanished from the very country that gave them birth.

Ancient European folk songs which antedated Luther and Bach and which came via the Pilgrims overseas, are whined in church, roared in taverns, and, in due course, are, sung in parts, after the refined and skillful madrigal manner, in the more cultivated New England circles. One of the most exquisite of all of the Scotch ballad songs, "Barbara Allen," finds its way over most of the States, which bestow upon it countless variations, both of verse and melody, and the ballad is met up with by John and Alan Lomax when a Negro convict sings them a song, "Bobby," whom the Negro, poetically speaking, mounts on a buckskin pony and buries in the Arizona desert, or, variously, ships as a corpse out of the railroad depot at Dallas, Texas, leaving her relatives "Squallin' an' holl'in' " with grief.* And a revival tune, like the minister in Shaw's "Devil's Disciple" is transported, first to the vaudeville stage, and then metamorphosed into the theme

* American Ballads and Folk Songs," by John and Alan Lomax.

8

song of the Spanish War, its disrespectable title, derived probably from thoughts of hell-fire, being "A Hot Time in the Old Town To-night." The songs are constantly changing in form and subject matter through the pressures of environment and circumstance. At the same time new songs are constantly being created, all from the mood or situation of the moment, and it is from such a source that our great composers spring.

We have then identified creations unparalleled in another nation's music, as, for instance, Emmett's "Dixie," the tune which that black-faced comedian of the pre-Civil War days penciled out on a piece of paper backstage as naturally as a Yankee farmer whittles a piece of wood among his cronies of the grocery store. For reckless laughter and high, nervous mood, there is no song that matches it. It is the tune of an American and only an American, the tune that conveys the essence of the old adage which saith that whereas an Englishman enters a house as if he owned it, the American enters the house as if he doesn't care who in hell owns it. (Was there ever a more fitting ceremony than the funeral of Dan Emmett, dressed in his minstrel's garb and the playing of "Dixie" as he was lowered into the grave?)

There is the roustabout's song of the Mississippi, "I'm Gwine to Alabamy, O," the song so wild and barbaric in its essence, with the lonely cry which seems to convey as nothing else could the mystery of the great river and the nostalgia of those who passed obscure or splendid lives on its stream and then vanished as one drop in its current to the sea. And the sailor man innured to the life of hard labor and brutal treatment, and the treacherous calms and rages of the sea, bawls to high heaven as he weighs the anchor, or pulls on the rope, of his miserable "dollar and a half a day," and shouts out an utterance so tremendous that it is the only equivalent we know in music to the line that closes "Moby Dick"— "the great grey shroud of the sea" that "rolled on as it had rolled for five thousand years."

It is regrettable but true that few of our trained composers of the more intellectual type have thus far been able to convey these truths, great or small, of our living. I remember a talk, very illuminating to me, with that famous American genius, the eminently popular John Philip Sousa, the march king. Of American-Portuguese ancestry, Sousa was not, in the strictest sense of the word, an intellectual. The composer of the marches which have sounded around the world, and which have never been paralleled for their swing and lift in any other country, had a set of very simple, straightforward and well-nigh religious convictions. He believed in God and in America as God's finest handiwork; in America's Army and Navy, and, with equal certitude, the Republican Party! He told me of the day when he was returning after his first world tour on an American ship to his America. On a cloudy morning he walked the deck and, looking upward, saw the American flag soaring against a windy and tumultuous sky; and there came to him, instantaneously, the melody which makes the middle part of "Stars and Stripes Forever!" The melody is not by Beethoven, but the inspiration of it and the truth of its expression are hardly to be surpassed. A melody? It is an ecstasy! It is the thing that swelled in the heart of that little man, so great in his fervor and simplicity, as he watched the streaming colors; it is the song of faith, with a wonderful line which neither rises nor falls, but maintains a progress as serene as that of the winged victory over the pulsation of the march accompaniment. Richard Strauss would have taken a full panoplied orchestra and a modern symphonic poem to do it. Schubert could have accomplished it with a few chords. Sousa had his own power.

I do not quote this melody as an example of the world's most distinguished art, but I would emphasize the fact of its genuineness and vitality, representing as they do, not only the emotion of an individual but a phase of the national experience. You can find in the marches and certain of the songs from Sousa's light operas the flavor of youthfulness, gaiety,

9

braggadocio, the cock-sureness, if you like, of America of the '90's in the flush of its success and its flirting with imperialism. It is part of us and our history and from those great origins it derives its being.

In the past twenty-five years, art music in America—the music of our studios, conservatories, concert halls and opera houses—has developed in a most impressive manner, and this with the rapidity and distribution probably unparalleled in a like period of time in the history of any other nation. This is extremely impressive, but much more impressive if we properly understand its profound significance which is the growth of our native and untutored art and the part that the spirit of our nation plays in it. Some day, these two different strata of the musical art will meet and mingle; in fact that process is advancing very propitiously. The signs of it are on every hand. It is shown in such a folk-opera as Jerome Kern's "Showboat," including that song which is already an acknowledged element of American folk lore, "Old Man River." It was presaged on the day in the year 1924, when we heard the first performance by the composer and the superb band of Paul Whiteman, of George Gershwin's "Rhapsody in Blue," with its opening theme of such color and twist and originality as to prove once and for all the erroneousness of the statement that a jazz melody could never have any real variety of rhythm, or distinction of style. It is demonstrated, from the other direction, by the manner in which radio and record and song-picture are making familiar and liked a hundred masterpieces by immortal composers. But it is good that this process is gradual and real in the life of our people. I deem it more fortunate than otherwise that the average American still deprecates his knowledge of art and protests that it is something rather beyond him and his experience. It is good that he will not deceive himself in these matters, that as a class he refuses to read a book or gaze at a picture or listen to an opera or symphony which does not say something to him. He is also inclined to be unaware of the justness of his own per-

ception when he tells you that he doesn't understand Milhaud and Hindemith and Stravinsky very well, and that for his enjoyment he's mainly obliged to fall back on the songs that he hears on the street and in the theatres, or the older melodies that he learned from his father and mother.

He is absorbing his music from the ground up and not the other way around. He is not being instructed in art for purposes of class education or snobbish, sterile, superficial culture. Only today, through the development of orchestras and with the machines of transmission already mentioned, is he becoming aware that the great foreign composers, whom he has held in such awe, also wrote for him and for their fellowmen in terms of a highly developed utterance which nevertheless had its true roots, just as he has his, in the common speech, the common thought, the common life and experience.

Meanwhile, what has happened to our popular music overseas is very significant. Let us ask ourselves what American music has made headway on the other side of the water? When in a bygone year, the Prince of Wales was welcomed at Pretoria, East Africa, the crowd was furnished with broadsides which carried Stephen Foster's "Oh Susannah" and "Old Folks at Home." And when European composers, leaders of their craft, sought for some nourishing material with which to refresh what one fears must be described as their present infertility born of the decadence and ultra-sophistication to which they have succumbed —when these individuals, with their quick appreciation of anything that might make possible some novel expression or effect of instrumentation, came over here, they made straight for Harlem and jazz was the principal subject of their conversation. The reference is to men like Honegger, Stravinsky, Ravel, in his last period, men fascinated by the vitality and novelty of our jazz music. It is a further fact of interest that all these men made experiments in the jazz style, in which they failed. But what could be a greater tribute to the idiom? Once upon a time this writer went searching in the

Caucasus for native Caucasian music, which is an extremely fascinating product. He was annoyed when the leader of a native orchestra branched from performances of Eastern music into some rather clumsy presentations of jazz. His annoyance increased to impatience when the native leader apologized for this divergence, asking obsequiously at the same time if the American gentleman, when he returned home, would very kindly forward some copies of the latest fox-trots from Broadway, which were difficult to secure in Tiflis. This is cited only as an example of the vitality and originality of an American form of dance music which has swept over the world and even, momentarily, submerged the popular musical expression of some communities overseas. It is not altogether a good omen. The Caucasian gentleman had tunes up his sleeve considerably more distinguished, if not more novel to him, than the ones he asked for. And there are nobler aspects of the musical art than jazz and much grander forms of musical expression that will come from us when our composers have achieved the great synthesis of a national expression which summarizes the fundamental accents of native art and the grander perspectives coupled with the technical resources which must enter into the equipment of the greatest creative musician.

Singularly enough, even in the direction of internationalism, our popular composers have showed our intellectuals a thing or two in a manner almost laughable for its ingeniusness and felicity. A composer or arranger of Tin-Pan Alley has heard Debussy or Rimsky-Korsakoff or Stravinsky in a concert hall or over the air. He suddenly realizes that there is a fancy chord or even an uncommon bit of contrapuntal procedure which will excellently set off a certain measure of his ditty, and in it goes. The result is native, contemporaneous and often witty. The point is that the composer has, in no sense, lost his own individuality or his own style by the appropriation.

(See, for instance, "Star Dust" or certain of the songs of George Gershwin.) That is the manner in which an international awareness can and should enrich a composer's expression, or extend his vocabulary, but it brings us back to the alpha and omega of creative art which must always be local, as well as personal in its origin, however universally significant its message.

It is not braggadocio and it is not flag-waving to say that it may well devolve upon us, more than any other people, to take up the torch of thought and art which has been almost quenched for the moment in the old world, and go forward to new tasks and the destiny of a people who know that a greater day for Mankind is not an impossibility, and the passing of ages is more than a cycle of experiment and error, aspiration and failure, returning ever in an evil circle to the self-same spot. A hundred and fifty years ago, Emerson cried out against American minds which still occupy themselves to the exclusion of their own intellectual possessions with "the sere remains of foreign harvests." He wanted a national and a democratic literature. He said, "I ask not for the great, the remote, the romantic; what is doing in Italy or Arabia; what is Greek art, or Provencal minstrelsy; I embrace the common; I explore and sit at the feet of the low."

We of America today must follow up that thought. The time is approaching now when we can work consciously toward, if not immediately achieve, a genuinely modern, all-inclusive and democratic culture; when we can put forever behind us the stratified living and thinking of the past which has brought about the present appalling destruction of its culture. In that day we will employ all the elements of knowledge and the fruits of experience provided from our national sources. Among them the scholars and artists and other citizens of the future will rank high the treasures of our popular music.

O. D.

About the Music

In THEIR native environment, folk songs are sometimes sung to guitar or banjo accompaniment, but far more often, without any harmony whatsoever. In such cases, the physical surroundings, the setting of the scene—whether it be railroad embankment, riverside shack, or mountain still—seem to complete the picture and make any other background unnecessary. But when lifted out of their natural setting and placed in the (to them) strange and bare atmosphere of the printed page, the simple melodies are often ill at ease. In composing the settings for these songs, I have preserved the tunes intact, while adding a harmonic background in the piano intended to supply the color originally provided by the physical background.

I have tried to compose settings that would fit the special environment in which each song arose. I have used as a guide historical and human clues arising out of the texts rather than any abstract musical rules. But often it was the tunes themselves that dictated the type of harmonization.

In the case of composed songs by Billings, Law, Emmett, Foster, Work, and others, I often found the original arrangements for one reason or another unfitted to the purposes of this book. Wherever possible I have adapted the choral or piano harmonies of the original setting, but I have not hesitated to compose entirely new arrangements when I felt they were needed.

For instance, the "Battle Hymn of the Republic" (John Brown's Body) as it is generally arranged in the traditional four part text-book harmony gives more the feeling of a Sunday school hymn tune than the militant song that men chanted while marching into battle. In my setting I have tried to catch the feeling of trumpets and drums, of raucous voices rising above the sounds of war.

In setting "Heave Away," I felt it should have the unfettered quality of strong men hard at work; in "Gwine to Alabamy" I thought of far-away, primitive voices floating over a wide river. In "Ground-hog" I heard the scrape of a lively fiddle; in "Oh Susannah," the rasping twang of banjos at a minstrel show; in "Alabado" the medieval seclusion of an old mission.

In some cases the harmonies may sound unconventional—there I have made them so because the songs themselves have come out of lives that have been strange and unconventional. Most of the songs in this book do not come out of the studio, the salon, the concert hall where the traditions of smooth, pleasant, euphonious musical style originated. The convict on a rock pile, the cowboy yelling at his herd, the farmer at a Saturday night barn dance, think little and care less about beautiful tone quality, blended harmonic colors, smooth phrasing—all those esthetic qualities that city people have come to expect from "good music." I have not tried to "civilize" the melodies that have come up out of the soil by dressing them up in polite, well-behaved harmonies. Where I heard the melodies raucous, I made the accompaniment equally so; where they are lyrical and sentimental, I have let the piano be so, too.

Of course, these harmonies are made as I felt them. Others will feel otherwise. They are welcome, and urged, to "roll their own." The same applies to all the indications of tempo, rhythm, dynamics, etc. They are intended as guides, and should be (and I have no doubt, will be) constantly disregarded by those who hear and see the songs differently. Folk music is flexible that way. Sung fast or slow, high or low, loud or soft, with sweet voices or way off pitch, it still manages to survive.

As to the melodies themselves: they are in all cases given exactly as I heard them sung or found them recorded, except in those cases where there were grossly obvious mistakes in notation. In some cases an obviously faulty barring has been rearranged,* in others, complex notation simplified.† In a few cases, the time values of an entire piece have been halved, ‡ as the old notation when played by pianists of average ability gave a far slower reading than the real tempo of the piece, as played and sung today, calls for. In one case ("David's Lamentation") the original time values have been doubled for the opposite reason.

However, it must be borne in mind that notations of folk music on paper can be only approximations at best. Those who have heard two folk singers sing the same song, or even have heard the same singer do the same number twice, know that there is not, and cannot be, any fixed or final version of any folk song, for the reason that this music by its very nature is ever varying, changing, growing. Unlike the composer, who sets his musical thoughts down on paper, thereby fixing the relationship of its tones and rhythms forevermore, the folk singer is constantly and instinctively adding to the songs he sings, embellishing them, changing them as his mood and memory dictate. In some singers the element of reproductive memory is strongest; in others personality and imagination play a larger role and from these we are apt to get so much unconscious variation and conscious improvisation that it is often a question whether their versions of old songs are really the old songs or something entirely new.

Songs keep on being born and disappearing with the seasons. Some melodies preserve their vitality over long periods of time, and the history of the various verses which are set to them is almost the history of a people.* Others flare up for a time, answering to the need of a moment, and vanish; among these may be some very beautiful and valuable ones.† Others disappear when the type of life or activity which called them into being and with which they are associated, dies out. ‡

At any rate, the selection of one version of a song rather than another can only be made on the basis of following one's musical instinct. And that, for better or worse, is what I have done.

The same holds true regarding the selection of verses accompanying many of the songs. Many folk songs have fluid texts: words which vary with almost every performance, or whole verses which come in or go out with the greatest of ease. Words of one song are often found tacked on to an entirely different tune. Sometimes roving verses or "floaters" are found which turn up in several different songs, often when you least expect them. Some songs have almost endless verses, for use on varying occasions (the record being held apparently by "Skip to My Lou" of which 160 verses are said to have been recorded). It is obviously impossible to print all the verses of all the songs. As in the case of the tunes, selection has been made on the basis of singability, value as Americana, variety and broad human appeal.

There is another reason why any written recording of our traditional music is always less than satisfying. That is because the true folk singer knows little and cares less about 4/4 time or do-re-mi-fa-sol. He often sings in a scale that is neither major nor minor, nor any other that can be played on the piano. Instead of singing whole or half tones, he often hits in between them, and the sliding pitches, the sudden catches, quirks and scoops in the voice, the characteristic intonations, form al-

---

* As in "The Dying Californian."

† The original notation of "John Hardy" contained double sharps!

‡ As in "Old Joe Clarke."

* I.e. "Yankee Doodle," "John Brown's Body."

† The runaway slave song, "Link O'Day," for example.

‡ The sea shanties, which passed from the status of active, functional music to that of entertainment and even of concert songs, when the old time sailing boats operated by manual labor gave way to the steamboat.

most the essence of folk style. These our common system of notation is utterly inadequate to express.

However it is the one we must rely on, if the music is to be read and played. We offer it therefore with one suggestion: when you sing the songs here presented, do not hesitate to "worry," embroider, or embellish the notes you see recorded, let the spirit move you!

E. S.

14

1. Plymouth Rock to Bunker Hill

For a long time it has been customary to look upon the first hundred and fifty years of white settlement on this continent as a period of complete cultural barrenness. Our forefathers—so the conventional story goes—were a dour, hard-working, God-fearing lot, who veered away from art and pleasure as devilish, and whose entire musical experience lay in the singing of a few dreary hymn tunes on Sundays, in between stretches of interminable sermons breathing repentance and hellfire.

Like all popular traditions, this one has a large element of truth. Early Plymouth and Salem were certainly no Viennas. There were no operas, no concerts, no chamber music in the homes. But modern scholarship has revealed the fact that the non-musicality of our early ancestors has been greatly exaggerated. The Pilgrim Fathers considered music so important that, while refugees in Holland and only several hundred strong, they brought out a special Psalm-book of their own.

Sung in Plymouth, many of these psalms were of rare, musical beauty, and were sung in lively and sparkling rhythms, with robust, hearty accents. As Carleton Sprague Smith has pointed out, psalm-singing was not only an act of worship, but "the favorite pastime at social gatherings" as well. Complex, madrigal-like versions of the psalms—for whose performance a high degree of musical skill was required—were sung in some early New England homes.

The period of earliest English colonisation —the first decades of the seventeenth century— was the height of the great musical Renaissance in the mother country. It was the time of Byrd, Gibbons and Morley, when every Gentleman was an amateur musician, expected to be able to sing madrigals at sight. No doubt the Cavaliers who settled Virginia and the South brought with them this high

musicality, for it was in the South that, some time later, the first recorded performance of an opera took place, the first musical society founded, the first regular playhouse established.*

Meanwhile, both in New England and in the South, the practice of ballad-singing was being actively pursued and folk song culture was in a flourishing state, as the repeated fulminations of the clergy against it inform us. As early as 1625, John Cotton inveighed against "lascivious dancing to wanton ditties, and amorous gestures and wanton dalliances." An early Plymouth court register recorded that one, Mercy Tubbs, "was to answer for mixed dancing." Almost a century later, Cotton Mather was still thundering from the pulpit against the "foolish songs and ballads" which "hawkers and peddlers carry into all parts of the country." These songs were apparently so attractive and popular that other New England preachers, adopting a different technique from Mather's, set up music committees in their congregations to gather the more appealing profane melodies to be fitted out with holy words and used as hymns—thus reviving the earlier practice of Martin Luther, who had said, "Why should the Devil have all the good tunes?"

Many of these popular ballads brought over by the early colonists from Europe recorded news events of the day. One of these related in song the story of the famous pirate Captain Kidd. Others dealt at length and in great detail with the loves and intrigues of noble lords and ladies. Singing the long narrative ballads was one of the few available forms of entertainment and pastime, and it provided not only "heart interest," but often was the only

*According to John Trasker Howard in "Our American Music."

15

means of passing on historical and other information. Songs also served for dancing, playing games, courting, spreading news, political comment, satire, scandal and what not.

While the circulation of these ballads was not as immediate as the popularization of songs today by radio, they were spread very widely throughout the thirteen colonies. Printed on sheets known as broadsides, in editions of many thousands, they were sold by peddlers in both town and country, at the democratic price of one penny. Collections of these ballads were imported to Boston in the 1680's, indicating that there must have been a large demand for them even before that date.

The appeal of these ballads in their day must have been as great as that of our own popular song hits. But unlike ours, they did not fade out with the passing season; they have been handed down by word of mouth for more than three hundred years, and are still found today in separated places such as Vermont, Florida, Michigan, Virginia and Texas. Their historical importance lies in the fact that they reveal a love of excitement and gaiety and a passion for romance not ordinarily associated with our early colonial forefathers. Their nature, too, shows that they were popular among the common people, where, perhaps, the strictures and restraints of a highly moral life were not so stern as among the righteous of the better classes. True, many of these ballads were originally brought over from Europe, but they have been so radically changed in the course of their transit from mouth to mouth that they have become thoroughly American in intonation and may be regarded as an integral part of our national culture.

Some of the earliest broadside ballads printed in this country can be identified as the work of known authors. Among these were two written in 1718 by a nine-year-old boy, Benjamin Franklin. Later he told of it: ". . . my brother . . . put me on composing occasional ballads. One was called the *Lighthouse Tragedy* . . . and the other was a sailor's song, on the taking of Teach (or Blackbeard) the pirate. They were wretched stuff, in the

Grub Street ballad style; and when they were printed he sent me about the town to sell them. The first sold wonderfully, the event being recent, having made a great noise." *

However, we have no record of contemporary composers of the tunes, if any. The first record of any original music written in this country comes from another source. This was the settlement of German mystics in the then wilderness of eastern Pennsylvania. One of their number, Johannus Kelpius, wrote the words and music of a series of hymns, called by the lugubrious title of "The Colloquium of the Soul with Itself" in 1697. Some forty years later, however, the first highly organized musical culture took root in America with the founding of the town of Bethlehem, Pennsylvania, by Moravian refugees from Switzerland and Germany. Although occupied with the most arduous tasks of clearing the wilderness and settling it, these early Americans found time every day for a *Singstunde*—an hour of communal singing.

Skilled musicians instructed the people in the art of choral singing, and formed them into such unusual instrumental ensembles as trombone quartets. Bethlehem was the first truly musical community in the United States, for it is recorded that the people worshipped, worked and played to music. In 1787, when New England divines were still debating whether or not congregational singing was fitting in the house of God, a little girl wrote, from her boarding school in Bethlehem: "I play the guitar twice a day; am taught the spinet and forte piano, and sometimes I play the organ." †

Early Bethlehem composers were the first to write music in the larger forms of cantata, string quartet, sonata, etc., in this country. But to this community music was not only entertainment or religion, it was a practical help in daily life. The constant fear of the early settlers was from attack and massacre by the In-

* Franklin: "Autobiography."

† Quoted by John Tasker Howard: "Our American Music."

dians. One Christmas Eve in the 1740's the story goes that news was brought to the settlement that a band of Indians had surrounded and was planning to attack and annihilate the colonists. With the ingenuity of pioneers, the people decided to send their trombone choir into the loft of the meeting house to play hymns, believing the unusual sounds would impress the superstitious Indians. The four trombonists played through the holy night, and at dawn the savages had vanished. They thought the awesome harmonies were the warning voice of some great deity.

Whether or not the story is true, it can stand as a symbol of the place of music in the big job of building America.

Who Is the Man?

*Arrangement
by Elie Siegmeister*

Moderately with Motion

Who is the man, that life doth will; That lov-eth dayes, good for to see?

Re-freyn-ing, Keep thy tongue from yll, Thy lips from speak - ing fal - la - cee.

Doo good and e - vil quite es - chew, Seek peace and af - ter it pur-sew.

2

In all time bless the LORD will I
His praise within my mouth, alway.
My soul shall in the LORD glory;
The meek shall heare, and joy shall they.
O magnifie the LORD with me
His name together extoll we.

WHO IS THE MAN?

THIS GRAND old tune came to America across continents, seas and centuries. It sounded through the trials and portents of the fateful Pilgrim voyage of 1620, and may well have rung across the waters of Plymouth harbor during the service conducted on the Mayflower by Elder Brewster on the cold Sunday of December 16, when a landing could not be made, and the faithful "cried out unto the Lord and He heard their voyce and looked upon their adversitie." For "Who is the Man?" was one of the hymns of the Ainsworth Psalter, the only book of printed music which the Pilgrims brought with them to America. Longfellow, in "The Courtship of Miles Standish," sees to it that John Alden, bearing the Captain's message, finds Priscilla with the volume on her knees.

Open wide on her lap lay the well-worn psalm-book of Ainsworth
Printed in Amsterdam, the words and the music together,
Rough-hewn, angular notes, like stones in the wall of a churchyard,
Darkened and overhung by the running vine of the verses.

The melody of "Who is the man?" is an ancient European folk-song which served Luther in 1539 for his chorale version of the Lord's Prayer. J. S. Bach treated it in fully a dozen different ways and included it in the score of his "Passion according to St. John." The Ainsworth version of the tune dates from the time when music was written without bar-lines. These Mr. Siegmeister has supplied, indicating the Rhythmic design thus cast in alternating 4-4 and 3-4 measures.

3

I sought JAH (Jehovah) and he me answered;
And from my fears all, rid me free.
To Him they looked and flowed;
And ashamed let not their faces bee.
JAH heard when this poor man did call:
And saved him from his troubles all.

4

Jehovah's angel camp doth lay,
'bout them that fear him; and frees them.
Taste ye and see that good is JAH:
O bless man, that hopes in him.
Fear ye Jehovah, saints of His:
For to his fearers, want none is.

5

Evil shall cause the wicked die:
And haters of the just man, they
Shall be condemned as guilty.
His servants soul, redeem doth JAH:
And they shall not be judged unjust,
All that in him for safety trust.

19

Confess Jehovah

Arrangement
by Elie Siegmeister

Con - tin - u - eth for - ev - er. To him that doth, him - self one - ly

Things won - drous great: for, His mer - cy Con - tin - -eth for - ev - er.

2

To Him that spread the earth more high
Than waters are: for His mercy
Continueth forever.
To Him that made great lights to bee:
Because His bountiful-mercie
Continueth forever.
The sun to have the soveraigntie
By day: for His benigne-mercie
Continueth forever.
The moon and starrs for soveraigntie
By night: for His benigne-mercie
Continueth forever.

CONFESS JEHOVAH

NOT ALL or even the greater number of the Puritan hymns were sung lugubriously. In most cases they were intoned with emphasis and vigor. And look at this tune, also from the Ainsworth Psalter. A lively tune, if no worse! A tune in which the godly might sniff brimstone, and mutter of "Geneva jigs." Yea! Even is it rumored that some of these psalm-tunes found their way out the church door, and could be heard echoing from taverns, to the accompaniment of unseemly mirth and the guzzling of strong waters. This melody had more than one association. It was known to the early Lutherans as a "Strassbourg tune," and in their French version became a war-song of the Huguenots. Chanted thus in camp and battlefield it earned the title in a later century of the "Huguenot Marseillaise." Though the text sits clumsily upon it, the two-fisted energy and forthrightness of the music may well have sustained the faithful through the trials and vicissitudes of life in the new land. Of such are the adventures of a folk-song!

3

To Him that with their firstborn-race
Smote Egypt: for His bounteous grace
Continueth forever.
And Israel bring forth did Hee
From mids of them: for, His mercie
Continueth forever.
With strong hand, and arm stretched-high:
Because His bountiful-mercie
Continueth forever.
To Him that parted the Red Sea
In parts: because, His kind-mercie
Continueth forever.

4

And caused Israel through to passe
Amids it: for, His bounteous grace
Continueth forever.
And threw Pharoh and his armie
In the Red Sea: for His mercie
Continueth forever.
To Him that in the wilderness
Did lead his folk: for His kindness
Continueth forever.
To Him, that kings of greatness-high
Did smite: for, His benigne-mercie
Continueth forever.

When Jesus Wept

Words and Music
by William Billings

Arrangement
by Elie Siegmeister

When Je - sus wept, the fall - ing tear

In mer - cy flow'd be - yond all bound;

When Je - sus groan'd, a trem - bling fear

Seiz'd all ye guil - ty world a - round.

This is to be sung by four voices. The first singer sings the song through twice. When he reaches the second line, the second singer starts at the beginning and does the same. When the second singer reaches the second line, the third starts, and so on.

WITH THIS eloquent setting in the form of a round of the sacred words, "When Jesus wept," there steps upon our scene one of the most rugged individualists in the history of American music—William Billings, of Boston. An artisan, self-taught in music, a flaming vortex of religious and patriotic feeling, he was as independent as they make 'em, and of an appearance as exceptional as his personality. He was one-eyed, with a game leg and arms of unequal length. His stentorian voice could bellow his music with deafening ardor. He broke the peace of a Boston Meeting House with his "fuguing tunes" which he roundly declared to be "more than twenty times as beautiful as the old slow tunes," and cited their effect upon "the audience, entertained and delighted, their minds surprisingly agitated and extremely fluctuated, sometimes declaring for one part and sometimes for another. . . . Oh ecstatic! Rush on, you sons of harmony!"

Rosa

Arrangement
by Elie Siegmeister

2

Rosa, willen wy minnen? Mint Rosa, mint Rosa.
Rosa, willen wy minnen? Mint Rosa, zoet!
Rosa med haer bloemenhoed—
Zy had de geld, maer weining good;
Danst Rosa zoet!
Rosa, willen wy minnen? Mint Rosa, mint Rosa.
Rosa, willen wy minnen? Mint Rosa, zoet!

3

Rosa, willen wy trowen? Trouwt Rosa, trouwt Ros
Rosa, willen wy trowen? Trouwt Rosa, zoet!
Rosa med haer bloemenhoed—
Zy had de geld, maer weining good;
Danst Rosa zoet!
Rosa willen wy trowen? Trouwt Rosa, trouwt Rosa
Rosa willen wy trowen? Trouwt Rosa, zoet!

24

ROSA

THIS SONG comes from the Dutch colony of New Amsterdam, where they were a little less afraid of merriment than in the colonies further north. In this locality, and very early, was to be found a diverse selection not only of hymns but of popular songs, ballads, dances, and children's games from the old world. The simplicity and innocence of the melody is that of an earlier time and perhaps a simpler and happier people than our own—today.

2

Rosa, will you be mine now, mine now, mine now?
Rosa, will you be mine now, O Rosa sweet!
Rosa with her hat of flowers
Has little wealth but happy hours,
And dances sweetly.
Rosa, will you be mine now, mine now, mine now?
Rosa, will you be mine now, O Rosa sweet!

3

Rosa, let us get married, married, married.
Rosa, let us get married, O Rosa sweet!
Rosa with her hat of flowers
Has little wealth but happy hours,
And dances sweetly.
Rosa, let us get married, married, married.
Rosa, let us get married, O Rosa sweet!

Lowly Bethlehem

Words by Count Zinzendorf
Music traditional

Arrangement
by Elie Siegmeister

LOWLY BETHLEHEM

THIS SONG has a remarkable story. It was apparently improvised on Christmas Eve, December 24, 1741, on a momentous occasion when the neighbors had gathered from miles around, to celebrate their holiday in the first house that the Moravians had built in the town now known as Bethlehem, Pa. This house, in its humble way, served almost the mission of the mediaeval cathedrals of Europe. It was a house adopted to purposes of worship as well as shelter and defense against foes for man and beast. People lived in one part of it, and their animals in another. The question had arisen and was being hotly debated as to whether the town, which has now a double fame as the site of the steel industry on one hand and the Moravian church on the other where the famous annual Bach festivals are held, should be named Jerusalem or Bethlehem. The story goes that in the midst of the service the leader of the community, Count Zinzendorf, who had a remarkable gift of extemporization, arose, and leading his followers to where the cattle were kept, improvised the melody and the words which begin *"Not* Jerusalem but Bethlehem where whence Jesus came to release us." And the narrative goes on to assert that the gathering was so profoundly moved that the name of Bethlehem was decided upon that night. This is believed to be one of hundreds of melodies composed in the spirit and style of the German chorale that were created by the German-Moravians who settled early in this country.

Nicht Jerusalem, sondern Bethlehem
Hat bescheret was uns nähret;
Nicht Jerusalem, werthes Bethlehem.
Du bist angemehn—
Aus dir kommet was uns frommet,
Werthes Bethlehem.

27

Barbara Allen

Arrangement
by Elie Siegmeister

'Twas in the mer - ry month of May, When all gay flo - wers were bloom - ing, Sweet Wil - liam on his death bed lay For the love of Bar - b'ra Al - len.

2

He sent a servant to the town
Where Barbara, she was dwellin'.
"My master's sick and sends for you
If your name be Barb'ra Allen."

3

So slowly, slowly she got up,
And slowly went unto him,
And all she said when she got there:
"Young man, I think you're dyin'."

4

"Yes, I am sick and low indeed
And death is on me dwellin';
No better, no better will I ever be
If I don't get Barb'ra Allen."

5

"Sir, do you remember the other night
In a gathering over yonder
You gave your gifts to all around,
And slighted Barb'ra Allen?"

BARBARA ALLEN

It was an embarrassing problem to make a final choice for this volume of the innumerable versions to be found in America of the exquisite song about the love and the cruelty and the tragic fate of Sweet William and Barbara Allen. The melody which is that of an old Scottish folk song, is one of the greatest treasures of the folk lore of Britain.

"Barbara Allen" was found in the Kentucky mountains by Cecil Sharp. In a myriad different forms, it is not confined to the Kentucky mountains, however. It is no wonder that the song has haunted the memory of men wherever the descendants of the British people went in America. Helen Harkness Flanders and George Brown have found many variants in Vermont and other of the New England states. There are other forms of the melody to be heard today. In Mississippi, Georgia, and Nebraska 98 versions have been taken down from the lips of untutored singers in Virginia alone, and the ballad has even been assimilated with characteristic alterations of text and tune by the American Negro.

Like the early Puritan melodies of this collection, this one bears witness to its age, by its "pentatonic" or five-tone scale, which omits the F-sharp and the C from its gamut, and also by the rhythmical freedom of the meter which clings so closely to the lilt of the words of the old ballad.

6

"Now you are sick and low indeed,
And death is in your dwellin';
No better, no better will you be
for you'll not get Barb'ra Allen."

7

He turned his face unto the wall,
While death was creeping o'er him;
He bid his friends adieu, and said:
"Be kind to Barb'ra Allen."

8

She hadn't got more than a mile from the place
Till she heard the death-bells ringing—
A ring and knock at ev'ry door,
Crying, "Woe to Barb'ra Allen."

9

She looked to the east, she looked to the west,
She saw the corpse a-coming.
"Set the lowly corpse down here
And let me look upon him.

10

"Go dig my grave both wide and deep,
Oh, dig it deep and narrow
Sweet William died for me in love
I'll die for him in sorrow."

11

Sweet William was buried in the high churchyard,
And Barbara buried by him,
And out of his grave grew a blood red rose
And out of hers a briar.

12

They grew and grew to the steeple top
Till they could grow no higher;
They lapped and tied in a true love knot—
The rose around the briar.

Tom Bolynn

Arrangement
by Elie Siegmeister

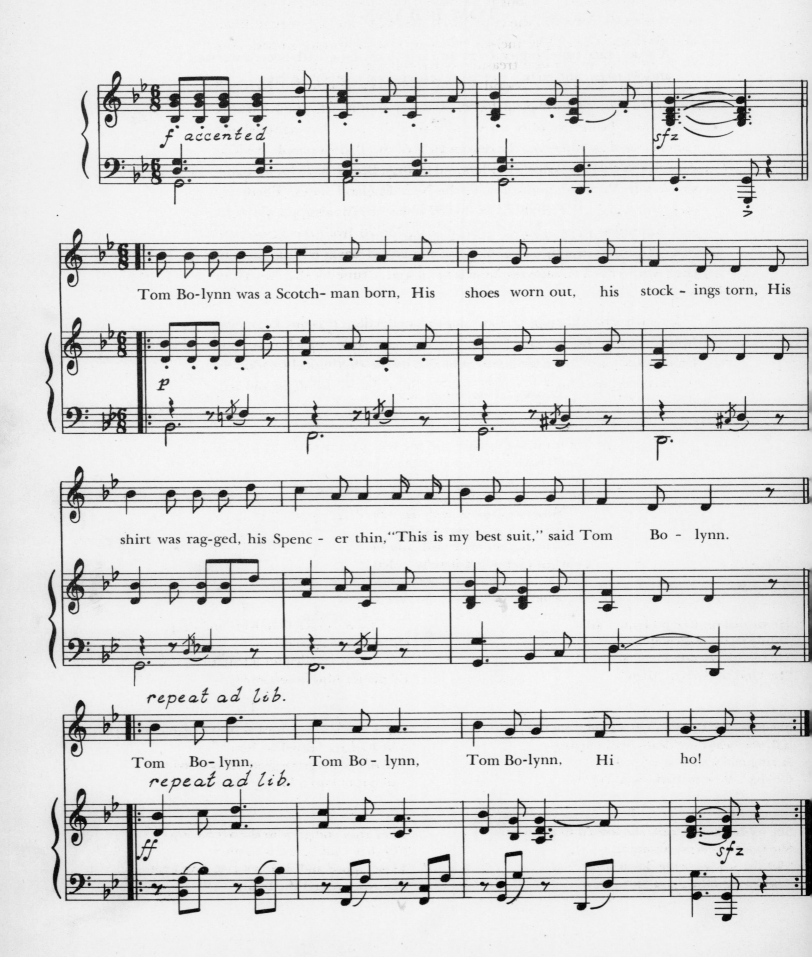

Tom Bo-lynn was a Scotch-man born, His shoes worn out, his stock-ings torn, His

shirt was rag-ged, his Spenc - er thin, "This is my best suit," said Tom Bo - lynn.

repeat ad lib.

Tom Bo-lynn, Tom Bo - lynn, Tom Bo-lynn, Hi ho!

TOM BOLYNN

A TART, racy tune, imported at an early date along with Scotch worsted and whiskey, and man's eternal revolt against mothers-in-law.

2

Tom Bolynn had no breeches to wear,
He bought a sheepskin to make him a pair,
The flesh side out, the fur side in,
"They are charming and cool," said Tom Bolynn.
CHORUS: Tom Bolynn, etc.

3

Tom and his wife and his wife's mother
Got into one bed together;
The weather was cold, the sheets were thin,
"I'll sleep in the middle," said Tom Bolynn.
CHORUS: Tom Bolynn, etc.

4

But his wife's mother said the very next day,
"You'll have to get another place to stay.
I can't lie awake and hear you snore.
You can't stay in my house any more."
CHORUS: Tom Bolynn, etc.

5

Tom got into a hollow tree,
And very contented seemed to be,
The wind did blow and the rain beat in,
"This is better than home," said Tom Bolynn.
CHORUS: Tom Bolynn, etc.

Springfield Mountain

Arrangement
by Elie Siegmeister

On Spring - field Moun - tain there did dwell A love - ly youth, I knowed him well. Too roo dee nay Too roo dee noo Too roo dee nay Too roo dee noo.

2

This lovely youth one day did go
Down to the meadow for to mow.

CHORUS: Too roo, etc.

3

He had scarce mowed quite round the field
When a pisen sarpint bit his heel.

CHORUS: Too roo, etc.

SPRINGFIELD MOUNTAIN

PROBABLY the first original American folk ballad to have been recorded in this country, based on the story of an actual occurrence. Timothy Merrick, son of Lieutenant Thomas and Mary Merrick, was bitten by a rattlesnake on Spring Mountain, August 7, 1761, and died within three hours, being at the time twenty-two years, two months and three days old and on the point of marriage. In its first form this ballad, whose author is identified as Nathan Torrey, was a sincere lament for the departed. It was widely adopted as a folk song. Somewhere about the 1840s the song reached the vaudeville stage and was parodied with highly exaggerated and melodramatic details. By this time it was not only the hero but also the sweetheart who met a horrible end. Then the vaudeville parody returned in some way to the populace, was again passed from lip to lip as a folk song, and in this comic version is found today all over the United States.

The grace notes and slides in the score are meant to indicate approximately the slides and scoops affected by genuine folk singers.

4
They took him home to Molly dear
Which made her feel so very queer.

CHORUS: Too roo, etc.

5
Now Molly had two ruby lips
With which the pisen she did sip.

CHORUS: Too roo, etc.

6
Now Molly had a rotting tooth
And so the pisen killed them both.

CHORUS: Too roo, etc.

Captain Kidd

*Arrangement
by Elie Siegmeister*

34

CAPTAIN KIDD

THIS IS one of the earliest of our bad men ballads. It originated at the time of William Kidd's trial and hanging for "murther and piracy" in 1701 in London. He it was who first captained an expedition to fight the pirates, then turned the tables and became one of the worst of them. He was quickly famous for terrible deeds, the news of which was spread via the grape-vine telegraph of the narrative ballad. Note the high moral tone and the gusto with which the hoister of the black flag relates his misdeeds and enjoins others to take warning from his fate. This rollicking ditty became very popular and is still to be heard in New England. It comes from a time when pirates might hang from the yard-arm or under more favoring circumstances land and "swagger the streets with impunity," for "the spending of the money they brought and the cheapness of the captured goods they sold brought them a following among rich and poor." (James Truslow Adams: "Provincial Society.") And they still hunt Kidd's treasure.

2

Oh! my parents taught me well, as I sailed, as I sailed,
Oh, my parents taught me well, as I sailed,
My parents taught me well to shun the gates of hell,
But against them I rebelled, as I sailed, as I sailed,
But against them I rebelled, as I sailed.

3

Oh! I murdered William Moore, as I sailed, as I sailed,
Oh, I murdered William Moore, as I sailed,
I murdered William Moore and left him in his gore,
Not many leagues from shore, as I sailed, as I sailed,
Not many leagues from shore, as I sailed.

4

And being cruel still, as I sailed, as I sailed,
And being cruel still, as I sailed,
And being cruel still, my gunner I did kill,
And his precious blood did spill, as I sailed, as I sailed,
And his precious blood did spill, as I sailed.

5

Oh! I steered from sound to sound, as I sailed, as I sailed,
Oh, I steered from sound to sound, as I sailed,
I steered from sound to sound, and many ships I found,
And most of them I burned, as I sailed, as I sailed,
And most of them I burned, as I sailed.

6

Oh! I'd ninety bars of gold, as I sailed, as I sailed,
Oh, I'd ninety bars of gold, as I sailed,
I'd ninety bars of gold, and dollars manifold,
With riches uncontrolled, as I sailed, as I sailed,
With riches uncontrolled, as I sailed.

Then fourteen ships I saw, as I sailed, as I sailed,
Then fourteen ships I saw, as I sailed,
Then fourteen ships I saw, and brave men they were,
Ah! they were too much for me, as I sailed, as I sailed,
Ah! they were too much for me, as I sailed.

8

Oh! to Newgate I am cast, and must die, and must die,
Oh, to Newgate I am cast, and must die,
To Newgate I am cast, with a sad and heavy heart,
To receive my just desert, I must die, I must die,
To receive my just desert, I must die.

9

Oh! Take warning now by me, for I must die, I must die,
Oh, take warning now by me, for I must die,
Take warning now by me, and shun bad company,
Lest you come to hell with me, for I must die, I must die,
Lest you come to hell with me, for I must die.

THROUGH ALL THE WORLD
(Captain Kidd)

2

See springs of water rise,
Fountains flow, rivers run;
The mist below the skies
Hides the sun;
Then down the rain doth pour
The ocean it doth roar,
And dash against the shore,
All to praise, in their lays,
That God that ne'er declines
His designs.

3

The sun, to my surprise,
Speaks of God as he flies;
The comets in their blaze
Give him praise;
The shining of the stars
The moon as it appears
His sacred name declares;
See them shine, all divine!
The shades in silence prove
God's above.

4

Then let my station be
Here on earth, as I see
The sacred One in Three
All agree;
Through all the world is made,
The forest and the glade;
Nor let me be afraid,
Though I dwell on the hill,
Since nature's works declare
God is there.

Locks and Bolts

Arrangement
by Elie Siegmeister

forced to lie with - out her.

LOCKS AND BOLTS

HERE IS a ballad of Colonial times, an old tale and an old tune which had great popularity in our early settlements and indeed will live long after these present settlers, as well as their ancestors, are gone. It has been sung and orally transmitted these 300 years and more in our country and there may easily have been that many years behind the time of its migration overseas.

The scale form, as will be seen, is precisely the same as that of "Barbara Allen," and there is a corresponding freedom in its rhythmical design, also, imperiously dictated by the rhythm of the poetical text. In all probability, as with the foregoing song, this one too is of Scottish origin.

2

Her yellow hair, like strands of gold,
Came rolling down my pillow.
She's the little one I love so well,
She's like the weeping willow.
"You've caused your parents to owe me a grudge
And treat me most unkindly,
Because you're of some high degree
And me so poor and needy."

3

I went into her uncle's house
Enquiring for my darling
The answer was: "She is not here,
I've no such in my keeping."
Her voice came from the roof above
Came straightway to the window,
"O love, O love, it's I'd be yours,
But locks and bolts doth hinder."

4

O passion flew, my sword I drew,
All in that room I entered,
O passion flew, my sword I drew,
All in that room I entered,
I took my sword in my right hand
All in that room I entered.
Come all young men that love like me
Fight on and take another.

5

Her uncle and three other men
Straightway after me did follow
Saying: "Leave this room, you villain, you,
Or in your heart's blood you shall wallow."
The blood was shed from every side
Till I got her from them.
And all young men who get such wives
Should fight till you overcome them.

Hangsaman

*Arrangement
by Elie Siegmeister*

Slack your rope, hangs-a-man, O, slack it for a-while; I think I see my fath-er com-ing, Rid-ing man-y a mile. "O, fath-er,* have you brought me gold? Or have you paid my fee? Or

40

have you come to see me hang-ing On the gal-lows tree?" "I

have not brought you gold; I have not paid your fee. But

I have come to see you hang-ing On the gal-lows tree."

HANGS A MAN

ONE OF the oldest and youngest of the English ballads. Its age is a good five hundred years and more. Its sentiment and naïvete have endeared it to the people of all the western nations. In America it is sung by whites and blacks, and is a favorite for children's game songs. They do not take too seriously the plight of the fair, who usually appeals in turn to father, mother, brother and sister for ransom money to escape the hangman.

Some versions tell the story the other way 'round: the man is in distress and his sweetheart comes to his aid with gold.

* NOTE: *The second, third and fourth verses are the same as the first, except that the words "mother," "sister," "brother" respectively, are substituted for "father."*

5

Slack your rope, hangsaman,
O, slack it for a while;
I think I see my true-love coming,
Riding many a mile.
"O, true-love, have you brought me gold?
Or have you paid my fee?
Or have you come to see me hanging
On the gallows tree?"
"Yes, I have brought you gold;
Yes, I have paid your fee,
Nor have I come to see you hanging
On the gallows tree."

My Days Have Been So Wondrous Free

Words: Traditional
Music by Francis Hopkinson

Arrangement
by Elie Siegmeister

My days have been so won - drous free, The lit - tle birds that fly With care - less ease from tree to tree Were but as blest as I, Were but as blest as

MY DAYS HAVE BEEN SO WONDROUS FREE

In 1788 Francis Hopkinson, poet, essayist, painter and man of society, Judge of the Admiralty of Pennsylvania and signer of the Declaration of Independence, sent a letter to his friend George Washington, in which he said, "However small the reputation may be that I shall derive from this work, I cannot, I believe, be refused the credit of being the first native of the United States who has produced a musical composition. If the attempt should not be too severely treated, words may be engraved on the back, and the arts in succession will take record and flourish amidst us."

Washington, replying, shrewdly avoided the responsibility of passing judgment on the songs dedicated to him, said, "My dear Sir: If you had any doubt about the reception your work would meet with or had the slightest reason to think that you should need any assistance to defend it, you have not acted in your usual good judgment in your choice of coadjutor for . . . I can neither sing one of the songs or raise a single note on any instrument to convince anybody. But I have one argument which will pervail with persons of true taste, at least in America. I can tell them that it is the production of Mr. Hopkinson. Your most obedient and humble servant, George Washington."

This at least proves the complete innocence of any musical pretensions on the part of the Father of his Country. As for Hopkinson's offering, it is a salon song of the period, polished and melodious, with a pretty sentiment, and suave and urbane as the tone of the above correspondence.

2. In Freedom We're Born

It was no coincidence that the first great outpouring of native song occurred at the time of the American Revolution. As long as the thirteen colonies looked to King George as their ruler and to England as their homeland, it was natural that their music should come from the country that nourished their social and economic life. But when the first feelings of American patriotism were born, after the arbitrary impositions and restrictions of the British Crown whipped up the resentment of the colonists to fever pitch, there came a surge of independent American song with it. The prejudice against all things British helped the new American composers and their works were greeted with intense enthusiasm.

The Sons of Liberty, organized in the 1760's to protest unjust and discriminatory taxation, found that satirical verses setting forth American grievances against the imperial crown, set to tunes of popular songs of the day, were an excellent means of furthering the cause of liberty. These works, printed on broadsides, and peddled and sung, at first surreptitiously, and then, as the struggle advanced, more and more openly, were the first American patriotic songs. The first of these, "The Liberty Song," written by John Dickinson, showed that in 1768 the Americans wanted, not independence, but freedom from unfair taxation—they were willing to pay, if they had a voice in allotting the share:

Our purses are ready. . . .
Not as slaves, but as Freemen our money
we'll give.

The Tories, scorning such pretensions, responded with military force, and immediately after the Boston Massacre, warned the people in song:

You simple Bostonians, I'd have you beware,
Of your Liberty Tree, I would have you take
care,
For if that we chance to return to this town,
Your houses and stores will come tumbling
down.

And the patriots, thoroughly aroused, issued the bold call for "a capital chop"—independence—and gathered in meeting halls to sing:

There's no knowing where this oppression
will stop.
Some say, there's no cure but a capitol chop;
And that I believe's each American's wish,
Since you've drenched them with tea and deprived 'em of fish.

The leaders of the American cause well understood the power of song, and did not hesitate to take time off from other duties to create American songs. Thomas Paine, author of "Common Sense," wrote one on the "Liberty Tree" and followed it with "Bunker Hill." That tireless enthusiast, Samuel Adams, organized the people of Boston into clandestine singing societies for the express purpose of learning the exciting new songs. Francis Hopkinson lampooned the British generals in his "Battle of the Kegs." Music heartened the Americans in their fateful undertaking.

When the struggle for independence finally did break out, the songs began to come thick and fast. The capture of Burgoyne, the victory of Paul Jones, the death of Nathan Hale, the surrender of Cornwallis at Yorktown and a score of other events became music on Americans' lips. Ironically enough, most of these songs were sung to tunes of English origin.

At the same time there appeared a man of a striking, aggressive personality and fiery conviction, who was to invent new, characteristic

American tunes for these songs. He was William Billings, the Boston tanner's apprentice who had started his musical career scribbling tunes on cowhides with chalk, and had gone on to astound the good citizens of Boston with his strange and exciting "fuguing tunes." Billings was renowned as one of the very first composers of original hymn tunes. The people were so amazed that there was a man among them who set down music he had himself thought up that they crowded into his singing school classes, and those who could not squeeze into the room listened outside the door. Apparently religion was on the side of the patriots, for the composers' inclusion of a defiantly rebellious song, "Chester," in his first published collection of hymns (engraved in 1770, incidentally, by Paul Revere) was greeted with great enthusiasm. He again combined religion and patriotism in his "Lamentation Over Boston," a paraphrase of the Biblical psalm, "By the waters of Babylon we sat down and wept, as we remembered thee, Oh Jerusalem," which read, "By the rivers of Watertown, we sat down and wept, as we remembered thee, Oh Boston." Ragged continental soldiers were cheered when they sang Billings' melodies which assured them that God was on New England's side:

We fear them (the British) not—we trust in God,
New England's God forever reigns.

The energies released by the Revolution expended themselves not only in the development of popular patriotic songs, but were applied, too, to the development of musical life in general and religious music in particular. One characteristic feature of music in those days was the country singing school, also initiated by Billings. Thousands of our ancestors received their first notion of music through this early American institution. Its democratic purpose was outlined by Billings who vigorously opposed the old custom of having only the deacon read from notes, while the congregation slavishly droned back the tunes

he had "lined out" to them. Said he: "As all now have books, and all can read, 'tis insulting to have the lines read in this way, for it is practically saying 'we men of letters, and you ignorant creatures.'"

The singing school was generally held under the guidance of an itinerant musician in the village tavern. "Those who attended were expected to bring their own candles. These were set on strips of board or inserted in an apple, turnip, or potato . . . To bring a tin or brass candlestick into the hall was scorned as a bit of aristocratic presumption." * Classes, often lasting three hours, were held for several weeks; young and old took part, beating time with the right hand while singing, and at the end of the period the town or village could boast a congregation that was able to read at least simple hymns in harmony by note. "Their voices were tremendous in power, issuing from ample chests and lungs, invigorated by hard labor and simple food, and unrestrained by dress. . . . It was no insignificant, tremulous voice, but grand, majestic and heart-stirring; and when applied to such tunes as *Old Hundred, Mear* and *Canterbury,* everything around seemed to tremble." †

So enthusiastic were these singing congregations that the teachers soon ran out of hymns, and took to writing new ones which were issued in collections published in a score of New England towns. As the number of tunes mounted, the composers, in order to distinguish them, named them after the towns or villages in which they were written. Thus we have the "Hartford Collection," the "Suffolk Harmony," the "Stoughton Collection," "Putney Hymn" and hundreds of others.

The modern reader, examining these old hymn-books, will be taken aback at first. Not only will he find harmonies which sound empty, strange, dissonant; he will find among the hymns certain complex, contrapuntal compositions (the so-called "fuguing tunes" referred to previously) in which the voices seem

* W. A. Fisher: "Ye Olde New England Psalm-tunes."
† Nathan D. Gould, one of the last of the old singing-teachers, as quoted by Fisher, *ibid.*

to enter and drop out, cross and criss-cross in a most perplexing manner. A long, apparently rambling solo will break out of the mass of sound in a most irregular and surprising way. Again, here is the handiwork of that inveterate experimenter, Billings. Tired of the constant march of dreary four voice harmony, he felt that if Americans could overthrow the British king, and do away with the traditions of the past, he could throw off the hand of musical tradition and create a new, more dramatic form. In a typical American statement, worthy of any young atonalist of today, he wrote:

"As I don't think myself confined to any rules of Composition laid down by any that went before me, neither should I think (were I to pretend to lay down rules) that any who come after me were in any ways obligated to adhere to them, any further than they should think proper. So in fact I think it best for every Composer to be his own Carver."

Apparently there were plenty of people who thought Billings was not a bad Carver, for his choral compositions were performed more often than those of any other native composer for more than a generation. And when they fell out of style in the cities, they lived on in the country districts, being reprinted in many a rural songster for at least a hundred and fifty years. The fuguing tune style which he invented had its limitations. It was often crude and primitive. But it had courage and zeal, often moments of striking beauty, and sometimes, within its scope, produced genuine little masterpieces, such as "Montague" and "Evening Shade."

The religious and patriotic songs of William Billings and his followers, Andrew Law, Timothy Swan, Jacob Kimball, Oliver Holden, Jezaniah Sumner—and many others—were the characteristic music of America in its moment of birth, and as such are of great interest.

The Liberty Song

Words by John Dickinson
Music by William Boyce

*Arrangement
by Elie Siegmeister*

Come join hand in hand brave A - mer - i - cans all, And rouse your bold hearts at fair Li - ber-ty's call; No ty - ran - nous acts shall sup - press your just claim, Or stain with dis-hon - our A - mer - i - ca's name.

In Free-dom we're born and in Free - dom we'll live, Our pur - ses are read - y.

Stead-y, Friends, Stead-y. Not as Slaves, but as Free men our mon - ey we'll give.

2

Our worthy Forefathers—Let's give them a cheer—
To Climates unknown did courageously steer;
Thro' Oceans, to deserts, for freedom they came,
And dying bequeath'd us their freedom and Fame.
CHORUS: In Freedom we're born, etc.

3

The Tree their own hands had to liberty rear'd;
They liv'd to behold growing strong and rever'd;
With transport they cry'd, "Now our witness we gain
For our children shall gather the fruits of our pain."
CHORUS: In Freedom we're born, etc.

4

Swarms of placemen and pensioners soon will appear
Like locusts deforming the charms of the year;
Suns vainly will rise, Showers vainly descend,
If we are to drudge for what others shall spend.
CHORUS: In Freedom we're born, etc.

5

Then join hand in hand, brave Americans all,
By uniting we stand, by dividing we fall;
In so righteous a cause let us hope to succeed,
For Heaven approves of each generous deed.
CHORUS: In Freedom we're born, etc.

6

All ages shall speak with amaze and applause,
Of the courage we'll show in support of our laws;
To die we can bear—but to serve we disdain,
For shame is to Freedom more dreadful than pain
CHORUS: In Freedom we're born, etc.

7

This bumper I crown for our Sovereign's health,
And this for Britannia's glory and wealth;
That wealth and that glory immortal may be,
If she is but just—and if we are but Free.
CHORUS: In Freedom we're born, etc.

THE LIBERTY SONG

THE LIBERTY SONG, besides being our first patriotic song, was the opening shot in the battle of ballads between patriots and Tories which preceded the outbreak of revolution. Written for the Sons of Liberty by
John Dickinson in 1768, it was published in the Boston Gazette of July
18, and soon brought forth a rejoinder.

Bandied back and forth, to the ancestral tune of "Hearts of Oak,"
were the taunts and defiances of the opposing camps. The final stanza of
Dickinson's poem, appearing in the Boston Gazette of July 18, said:

> *This bumper I crown for our sovereign's health,*
> *And this for Brittania's glory and wealth;*
> *That wealth and that glory immortal shall be,*
> *If she is but just, and we are but free.*

Soon a Tory parody appeared in the same paper:

> *Come shake your dull noddles, ye pumpkins, and bawl*
> *And own you are mad at Fair Liberty's call;*
> *No scandalous conduct can add to your shame,*
> *Condemnd to dishonor, inherit your fame.*

The patriot's retort, "The Parody Parodized," was published not only
in America, but in a November issue of the St. James' Chronicle,
London.

> *Come swallow your bumpers, ye tories and roar*
> *That the sons of fair Freedom are hampered once more;*
> *But know that no cut-throats our spirits can tame,*
> *Nor a host of oppressors shall smother our fame.*

What A Court Hath Old England

Tune of "Derry-down"

*Arrangement
by Elie Siegmeister*

What a court hath old Eng - land of fol - ly and sin, Spite of Chatham and Camden, Barre, Burke, Wilkes, and Glynn! Not con-tent with the game act, they tax fish and sea, And A - mer - i - ca drench with hot wa - ter and tea. Der - ry down, down, down der - ry down.

WHAT A COURT HATH OLD ENGLAND

A Tory satire which marked the ineffective efforts of the patriots in 1770, occasioned this reply from the Colonists. It was flung far and wide on broadsides and it added fuel to the rapidly rising flame of resentment when the British Parliament rejected the petition of 1775 and declared that a state of rebellion existed in America. Again an English tune, its hearty and muscular spirit emphasized by the characteristic refrain, "Down, Derry, Down," is the vehicle of the popular feeling. The song, fierce and satirical, was a recapitulation of grievances and a further enticement to war.

2

There's no knowing where this oppression will stop;
Some say "There's no cure but a capitol chop,"
And that I believe's each American's wish,
Since you've drenched them with tea, and depriv'd 'em of fish.
Derry down, down, down derry down.

3

Three Generals these mandates have borne 'cross the sea,
To deprive 'em of fish and to make 'em drink tea;
In turn, sure, these freemen will boldly agree
To give 'em a dance upon Liberty Tree.
Derry down, down, down derry down.

4

Then freedom's the word, both at home and abroad,
So out, every scabbard that hides a good sword!
Our forefathers gave us this freedom in hand,
And we'll die in defense of the rights of the land.
Derry down, down, down derry down.

YOU SIMPLE BOSTONIANS *

2

Our fleet and our army, they soon will arrive—
Then to a bleak island, you shall not us drive,
In every house you shall have three or four,
And if that will not please you, you shall have half a score.
Derry down, down, down derry down.

This song was the Tory original to which "What A Court Hath Old England" was a reply.

Yankee Doodle

Composer: Unknown

*Arrangement
by Elie Siegmeister*

Fa - th'r and I went down to camp, A - long with Cap - tain Good - 'in, And

there we saw the men and boys As thick as has - ty pud - din'.

Yan - kee Doo - dle keep it up, Yan - kee Doo - dle dand - y,

Mind the mu - sic and the step, And with the girls be hand - y.

YANKEE DOODLE

THIS BRISK and waggish tune, of which the authorship has never been established, but which nevertheless points to an English origin, played a dramatic and ironical part in the American Revolution. It was sung derisively by the English at the Yankees. They, in turn, struck up the tune as they marched the defeated British soldiers to prison. "They even enticed away the British band," says Marjorie Barstow Greenbie, "hired it themselves, and had it playing the obnoxious song." The Minute Men of Concord adopted it as their own, and when Cornwallis surrendered at Yorktown, it was to the accompaniment of "Yankee Doodle."

2

And there we saw a thousand men,
As rich as Squire David;
And what they wasted ev'ry day,
I wish it could be savèd.

3

And there was Captain Washington
Upon a slapping stallion,
Agiving orders to his men;
I guess there was a million.

4

And then the feathers on his hat,
They looked so 'tarnal fine, ah!
I wanted peskily to get
To give to my Jemima.

*The following verse is popularly known
in more recent times.*

Yankee Doodle went to town
Riding on a pony
Stuck a feather in his hat
And called it macaroni.

Chester

Words and Music
by William Billings

*Arrangement
by Elie Siegmeister*

Let ty-rants shake their i-ron rods, And slav-'ry clank her gall-ing chains. We fear them not we trust in God. New Eng-land's God for e-ver reigns.

CHESTER

Composed as a church hymn in 1770, it was caught up by the Minute Men on the march and sung by thousands of foot weary continentals from Maine to Georgia. Published in "Billings' Singing Master's Assistant," a collection of church music in general use in New England during the Revolution, the four-part singing hymn tune style in which this piece is set, must certainly have been sung in unison by the soldiers. The New England troops stationed in the Southern States, knew many of Billings' songs by heart and passed many an hour in setting them forth.

2

Howe and Burgoyne and Clinton too,
With Prescott and Cornwallis joined,
Together plot our overthrow
In one infernal league combined.

3

The foe comes on with haughty stride,
Our troops advance with martial noise;
Their vet'rans flee before our youth,
And gen'rals yield to beardless boys.

4

When God inspired us for the fight,
Their ranks were broke, their lines were forced.
Their ships were shatter'd in our sight
Or swiftly driven from our coast.

Bunker Hill

Words by Nathaniel Niles
Music by Andrew Law

Arrangement
by Elie Siegmeister

58

BUNKER HILL

YOUNG ANDREW LAW had just received his B. A. from Rhode Island College in September 1775, when the battle of Bunker Hill made the good citizens of Boston realize that the war was definitely on. Law sat down and set to music the stately and sonorous Sapphic ode, "The American Hero," by Nathan Miles of Norwich, Connecticut. The song caught the mood of the moment. Its timeliness connected it with the battle which had just been fought. After that the people simply called it "Bunker Hill." The austere harmonic treatment of this air by Mr. Siegmeister follows the scheme of the original choral setting. The stark chords and passing dissonances are notable.

2

Now, Mars, I dare thee, clad in smoky Pillars,
Bursting from Bomb-Shells, roaring from the Cannon,
Rattling in Grape Shot, like a Storm of Hailstones,
        Torturing Aether!

3

While all their Hearts quick palpitate for Havock,
Let slip your Blood Hounds, nam'd the British Lyons;
Dauntless as Death stares; nimble as the Whirlwind;
        Dreadful as Demons!

4

Still shall the Banner of the King of Heaven
Never advance where I'm afraid to follow:
While that precedes me with an open Bosom,
        War, I defy thee.

5

Fame and dear Freedom lure me on to Battle.
While a fell Despot, grimmer than a Death's Head,
Stings me with Serpents, fiercer than Medusa's:
        To the Encounter.

6

Life, for my Country and the Cause of Freedom,
Is but a Trifle for a Worm to part with;
And if preserved in so great a Contest,
        Life is redoubled.

Ode to the Fourth of July

Words by Daniel George
Music by Horatio Garnett

Arrangement
by Elie Siegmeister

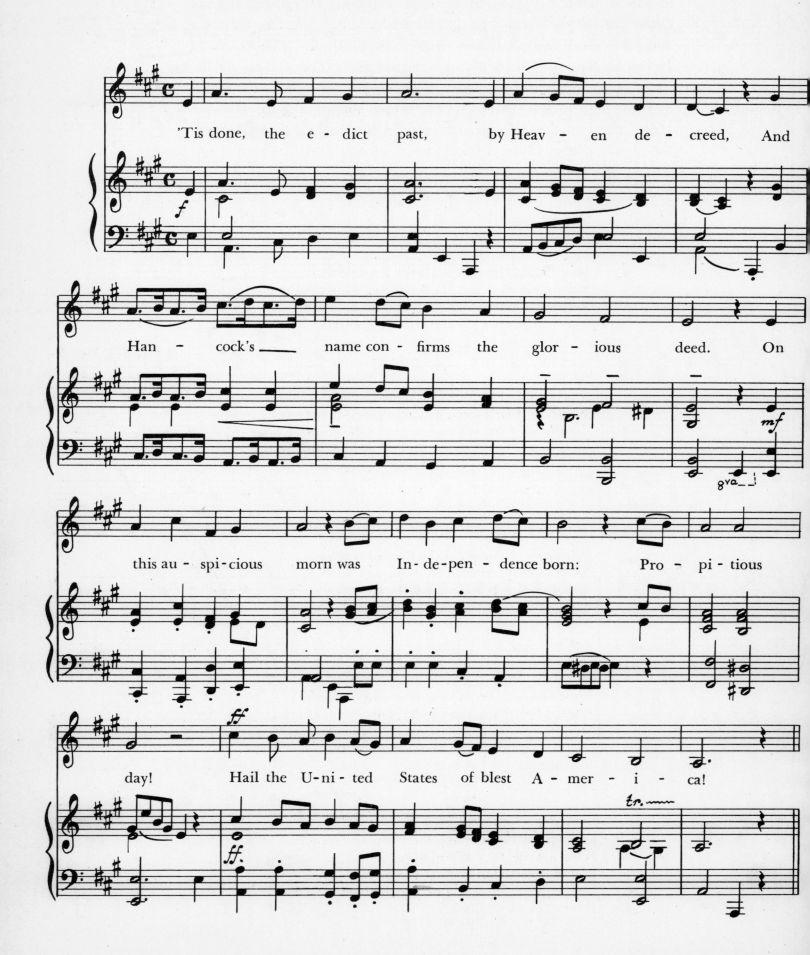

'Tis done, the e - dict past, by Heav — en de - creed, And

Han — cock's ___ name con - firms the glor - ious deed. On

this au - spi - cious morn was In - de - pen - dence born: Pro - pi - tious

day! Hail the U - ni - ted States of blest A - mer - i - ca!

Fly! Fly! Fly, swift winged Fame, The news

_ the news pro - claim. From shore to shore let can - nons

roar, And joy - ful voi - ces shout Co - lum - bia's

name. Shout! Shout! Co-lum-bia's name. Co - lum - bia's name,

ODE TO THE FOURTH OF JULY

AMERICA'S FIRST Fourth of July as a nation was greeted by this song, composed by Howard Garnet for the celebration of 1789. That was the day also, of the adoption of the new Constitution. Garnet's obscurity as a composer is such that he is not mentioned again in the history of American music. He will nevertheless be well remembered for this piece of inspiration, which rises imposingly to its climax with the final apostrophe, "Let cannon roar and joyful voices shout Columbia's name." There are trumpets and drums in the music, and the jubilant Handelian figures of the accompaniment here provided, carry out this latent feeling.

2

See haughty Britain, sending hosts of foes,
With vengeance arm'd, our freedom to oppose;
But Washington, the Great, dispelled impending fate, and spurned each plan.
Americans combine to hail the godlike man.
CHORUS: Fly! Fly, etc.

Ode On Science

Words and Music
Jezaniah Sumner

Arrangement
by Elie Siegmeister

The morn - ing sun shines from the east, And spreads his

glor - ies to the west. All nat - ions with his beams are

blest, Where' - er his rad - iant light ap - pears. So Sci - ence

crown the young and ris - ing States With lau - rels of im - mor - tal day!

The Brit-ish yoke, the Gal - lic chain, Was urged u - pon our necks in vain; All

f - p

- ty ty - rants we dis - dain, And shout, "Long live A - mer - i - ca!"

f

ff

1.

2.

shout, "Long live A - mer - i - ca!" ____

ff

David's Lamentation

Words and Music
by William Billings

Arrangement
by Elie Siegmeister

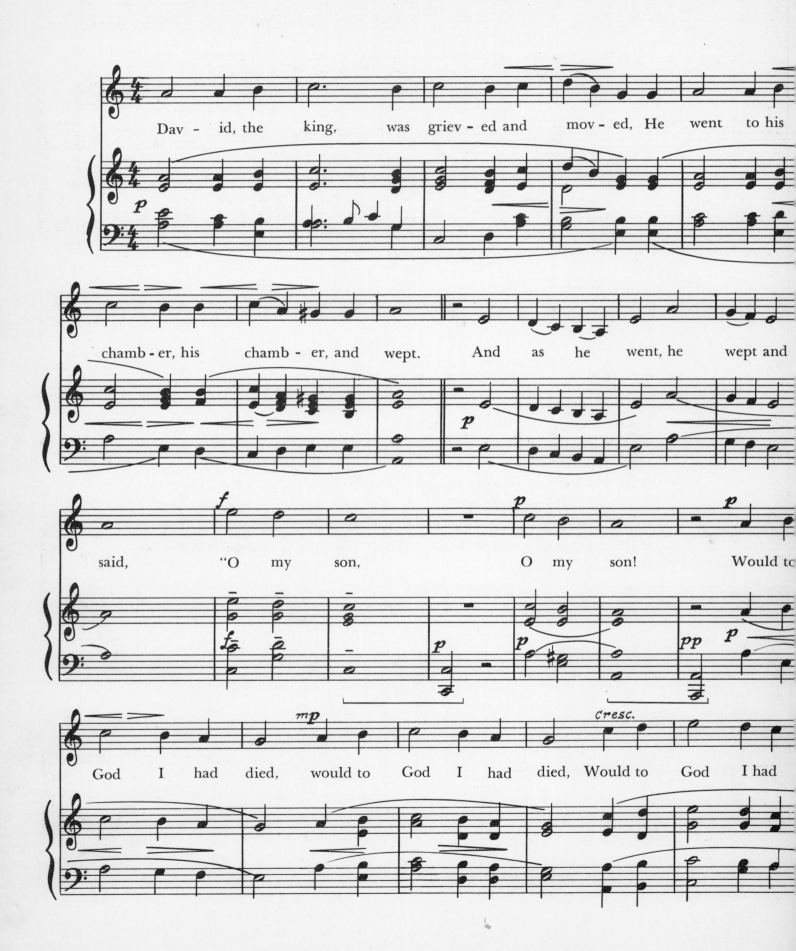

died   for   thee,   O   Ab - sal - om,   my   son,   my   son."

DAVID'S LAMENTATION

WHEN BILLINGS ATTEMPTED, as he did, musical settings of the Song of
Songs, he was out of his bailiwick. But when it came to the expression of
sincere and often noble emotion he wrote with a genuineness and simplicity that were moving. This setting of the verse of David's Lamentation is not only practicable to sing for those who are not accomplished
musicians, but it also expresses feeling with a dignity and earnestness
that more celebrated composers might envy. The present harmonization
follows carefully that of the choral setting.

Putney Hymn

*Arrangement
by Elie Siegmeister*

68

PUTNEY HYMN

Owing to the lack of instruments in the churches, the scarcity of printed music, and attendant circumstances, congregational singing at a certain time in New England had sunk to a low level. To remedy this, itinerant deacons who specialized in teaching the elements of singing were sent from town to town. They would spend a few weeks in each community trying to set matters right and then would go on. These singing teachers were in many cases composers, and church music the one channel which New England morality permitted them for self-expression. The number of the hymns they composed went into the thousands. In order to distinguish them one from another they would be called by the name of the village at which the teacher was staying when the hymn was written. In this way the names of hundreds of tiny Vermont, Massachusetts and Connecticut hamlets are recorded in the hymnals. That is the origin of the grave "Putney," the noblest of the New England hymns.

The Bee

Arrangement
by Elie Siegmeister

As cu - pid in a gar - den strayed Trans - port - ed with the dam - ask shade, A lit - tle bee un - seen a - mong The silk - en weeds his fin - ger stung.

70

THE BEE

A SONG of the more fragile, delicate type, charmingly written for voice
and harpsichord, voicing the sentiments which must have gone well with
powdered wigs, knee breeches, tallow candles and federalist sentiments,
and a period and culture that are vanished. It first appeared in the
American Musical Miscellany in 1798, which was "a collection of the
most approved songs and airs, both old and new," printed by Daniel
Wright & Co., Northampton, Massachusetts.

2

As tears his beauteous cheeks ran down,
He stormed, he blowed the burning wound;
Then flying to a neighboring grove
Thus plaintive told the queen of love:

3

"Ah, ah, mama, ah me, I die!
A little insect, winged to fly—
It's called a bee, on yonder plain
It stung me. Oh! I die with pain."

4

Then Venus mildly thus rejoined,
"If you, my dear, such anguish find
From the resentment of a bee,
Think what those feel who'r' stung by thee."

Jefferson and Liberty

Arrangement
by Elie Siegmeister

The gloom- y night be - fore us flies, The reign of ter - ror now is o'er; Its gags, in - quis - i - tors, and spies, Its herds of harp - ies are no more! Re - joice! Co - lum - bia's sons, re - joice! To

ty - rants nev - er bend the knee, But join with heart, and

soul, and voice, For Jef - fer - son and Lib - er - ty.

JEFFERSON AND LIBERTY

JEFFERSON AND LIBERTY: homage to the plain man and champion of democracy whom the people loved so well, and by whom he was not held in the less regard for riding to his inaugural in Washington on horseback and receiving ambassadors in his bedroom slippers. The song has much of historical significance, narrating, as it does, the public detestation of the Alien and Sedition Laws which Jefferson had passionately swept away when he came into power. The vigor and zest of the music suggests a wild Irish jig converted into an air of a marked virility and driving power.

2
No lordling here, with gorging jaws,
Shall wring from industry the food;
Nor fiery bigot's holy laws
Lay waste our fields and streets in blood!
CHORUS: Rejoice, etc.

3
Here strangers from a thousand shores,
Compelled by tyranny to roam,
Shall find, amidst abundant stores,
A nobler and a happier home.
CHORUS: Rejoice, etc.

4
Here Art shall lift her laurel'd head,
Wealth, Industry, and Peace divine;
And where dark, pathless forests spread,
Rich fields and lofty cities shine.
CHORUS: Rejoice, etc.

5
From Europe's wants and woes remote,
A friendly waste of waves between,
Here plenty cheers the humblest cot,
And smiles on every village-green.
CHORUS: Rejoice, etc.

3. Thar She Blows

"Start her, start her, my men! Don't hurry yourselves; take plenty of time—but start her! Start her like thunder-claps, that's all. . . . Start her now; give 'em the long and strong stroke, Tashtego. Start her, Tash, my boy—start her, all; but keep cool, keep cool—cucumbers is the word—easy, easy—only start her like grim death and grinning devils, and raise the buried dead perpendicular out of their graves, boys—that's all. Start her!"

From Herman Melville's "Moby Dick"

FROM THE BEGINNING, Americans have been a sea-going tribe. When the Pilgrims came to Plymouth, they planned to live by catching fish and shipping it back to Europe. The first food they found in the New World was clams taken from Plymouth Bay. It was ship-building and sea-borne commerce that built up early New England. Timber was plentiful in Maine and out of it shrewd Yankee traders began at an early date to build the great square-sterned whalers that sailed out of New Bedford and Nantucket in search of the valuable oil that was so important to early industry. Meanwhile Bangor, Portsmouth, New London, Boston were sending out the square-riggers that soon began to compete with British-owned boats in the European and West Indies trade.

Life on the early sailing vessels was hard. The Yankee skipper was a man who believed in rigid discipline, generally enforced by no milk-and-water methods. The cruelty on some of the boats earned for them the description of "hell afloat." The food was "chiefly salt beef, salt fish, slumgullion, a ration of lime juice, a ration of grog . . . and always hard-tack." *

The sailor's work was brutally hard, and never-ending: "swabbing down decks, mending tackle, manning the pumps, heaving the lead, and always adjusting canvas to catch a favoring wind." *

Shanty-singing was, of course, not an American invention. Sailors had sung to help themselves at work ever since the days of the old Roman triremes. But the exciting period of the growth of the American navy from 1812 to 1860, the North Atlantic packet trade, the cotton traffic between Liverpool and the South, the height of the whaling industry, the golden days of the Yankee Clipper, and the shipping boom brought on by the gold rush around the Horn in '49—all of these brought ever more American men and ships to the sea and carried the practise of shanty-singing to its highest level.

Shanty-singing was not, as members of some choral societies may romantically imagine, a matter of giving vent to one's love of the sea in song. It was rather, as Joanna Colcord has pointed out, "a practical necessity in the work that daily and hourly went forward." † Everything on the old sailing boats was done by man-power and pulling together was essential if the ships were to be sailed. The singing of shanties with their vigorous and clearly-measured rhythms established the regular timing so necessary for the efficient execution of such tasks as weighing anchor, hoisting sail, manning the pumps and other work requiring split-second team-work.

The shantyman was that member of the crew whose voice, memory and skill in extemporizing apt or humorous lines singled him out above all the others. Most of the shanties were divided into solo phrases taken by the shantyman while the sailors were preparing their grip on the line, and a chorus, on which "all hands

* Linscott: "Folk Songs of Old New England."

* Linscott: "Folk Songs of Old New England."
† Colcord: "Songs of the American Sailorman."

gave a mighty pull and 'brought her home.' " *
Without the rhythm of the music, the heave or
drag would not have the absolute precision of
timing needed to throw the entire weight of
every man on the line at the same instant.

The shanties were of several varieties. The
"short-drag" shanties like "Haul on the Bow-
line" were used when only a few rapid, heavy
pulls were required. "Halliard shanties" (such
as "Blow, Boys, Blow") were used for the
longer and heavier tasks such as "catting" the
anchor and hoisting sail. The "Capstan" or
"Windlass" shanties were those used for a long,
steady process like hoisting anchor or "warping
ship" when the men wound the rope on the
capstan by walking around it, pushing the bars
before them. These were generally longer
songs, adapted to the tediousness and monotony
of the work.

In addition to the shanties which were
actually sung at work, there were the "fo'c'sle
songs" sung for entertainment in the hours
when the crew was off duty. While the rhythm
and character of the shanties were determined
by the nature of the work to which they were
adapted, the fo'c'sle songs were of varied
nature. They might be ballads, patriotic or
vaudeville songs or what not brought from
shore and in the course of time fitted out with
new words pertaining to sea life. They ranged
all the way from songs about ladies of easy vir-
tue, through epics of fishing and whaling, to
ballads of sea tragedies and victories of American naval heroes such as Paul Jones, Farragut
and Decatur.*

There is still much difference of opinion
about the origin and even the spelling of the
word "shanty"—or "chantey," about the
sources of the tunes themselves, the English or
American character of the songs. The begin-
nings of many of the songs are lost in the mists
of time, and early records are practically non-
existent. Shanties were sung on English vessels
long before there was an American navy, and
this has led British collectors to assume that *all*
shanties must have originated in their country.

But how explain the singing of a song such as
"Paul Jones Victory"—openly boasting of Yankee superiority—by British seamen? What is
there British about the lines,

> We'll receive a broadside from this proud
>   Englishman,
> And like true Yankee sailors, return it again.
> Hurrah! hurrah! Our country (America) for-
>   ever, hurrah!*

British authorities have suggested they may
have been new words fitted to an old English
tune. But then what of songs whose whole spirit
is Negro, like "A Dollar a Day" or "Run with
the Bullgine"; or minstrel-like shanties, and
those that resemble Stephen Foster, like "Sacra-
mento?" "Shenandoah" one of the most beautiful and widely-sung of all shanties on ships flying both the Union Jack and the Stars and
Stripes, speaks of crossing "the wide Missouri"
—which hardly flows through Kent or Cornwall.

The answer may be simple. American and
British boys worked interchangeably on ships
of both nations. In the early days, the English
language and English songs were the heritage of
both. With the coming of independence and
the growth of our own navy, songs of distinctly
American origin, reflecting American experiences and view-points were added to the store,
and British sailors working under a Yankee
shantyboy learned and sang such lines as,

> To us they (i.e. the British) did strike and
>   their colors haul down
> The fame of Paul Jones to the world shall be
>   known.
> His name shall rank with the gallant and
>   brave
> Who fought like a hero our country (i.e.
>   America) to save.
> Hurrah! Hurrah! Our country forever, hur-
>   rah!

and thought nothing of it. The sailorman was
more concerned with the tune, the swing and
go of a song, than with its nativity.

Whether American or English in national-

---

* We are indebted to Joanna Colcord's book, "Songs of
the American Sailorman" for much of this material.

*A notation of this song as sung by a British sailor to
Percy Grainger is found among a manuscript group of folk
songs collected in England by the eminent pianist, and now
in the New York Public Library.

ity, many of the songs have definitely Irish and Negro qualities. This is not surprising, for the sons of Erin and of the South had the full-throated or silvery voices that marked them out as obvious selections for the choice position of shantyman. It was natural that they should mingle familiar strains of their own people with the store of shanties which their memories held.

At any rate, whatever their origin or character, shanties have played a unique role in American life. They serve as enduring monuments to the great days of sailing the Yankee Clipper, and Moby Dick.

Hornet and Peacock

Arrangement
by Elie Siegmeister

Ye De - mo's at - tend and ye Fed - er - als, too; I'll sing you a song that you all know is true, Con - cern - ing the *Hor - net*, true stuff I'll be bail, That hum - bled the *Pea - cock* and low - ered her tail. "Sing hub - ber, O bub - ber," cries old Gran - ny Weal, "The *Hor - net* can tick - le the

Chorus

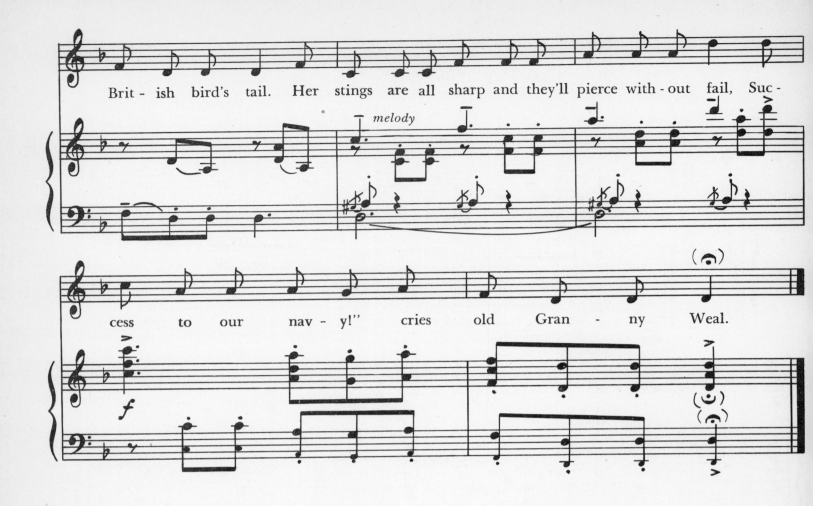

Brit-ish bird's tail. Her stings are all sharp and they'll pierce with-out fail, Suc-

cess to our nav-y!" cries old Gran-ny Weal.

THE HORNET AND THE PEACOCK

A BALLAD of the War of 1812 which tells of the contest between the
American ships "the Hornet" and "The Wasp," which brought the
British frigate "Peacock" to grief. It has all the salt and tang of the
cocky, swaggering New England sailormen, and the accompaniment to
the concise dance-like tune is intended to suggest the pricks and stings
of the hornet and the wasp.

2

This bird it was bred in the land of King George,
Her feathers were fine, her tail very large;
She spread forth her wings, like a ship in full sail,
And prided herself in the size of her tail.
"Sing hubber, O bubber," cries old Granny Weal,
"The *Hornet* can tickle the British bird's tail.
Her stings are all sharp, and they'll pierce without fail,
Success to our navy!" cries old Granny Weal.

3

King George then says, "To America go,
The *Hornet*—the *Wasp* is the British king's foe;
Pick them up, my dear bird, spread your wings to the gale."
"But beware of those insects," cries old Granny Weal.
CHORUS: "Sing hubber," etc.

4

Away flew this bird at the word of command,
Her flight was directed to Freedom's own land;
The *Hornet* discover'd her wings on the sail,
And quickly determined to tickle her tail.
CHORUS: "Sing hubber," etc.

5

So at it they went, it was both pick and sting,
The *Hornet* still working keen under her wing;
"American insects," quoth she, "I'll be bail,
Will humble the King bird, and tickle her tail."
CHORUS: "Sing hubber," etc.

6

The *Peacock* now mortally under her wing,
Did feel the full force of the *Hornet's* sharp sting;
She flattened her crest like a shoal on the wail,
Sunk down by her side and lowered her tail.
CHORUS: "Sing hubber," etc.

7

Here's success to brave Lawrence, who well knew the nest,
Where the *Hornet* and *Wasp* with honor still rest.
We'll send them with force, and with skill, I'll be bail,
Will humble King George, and tickle his tail.
CHORUS: "Sing hubber," etc.

BLOW BOYS BLOW

A HALLIARD SHANTY that originated in the old Congo slave trade. It told of the brutal life aboard the early Yankee sailing boats. During the Civil War the verse,

> *What do you think she's got for cargo?*
> *Old shot and shell, she breaks the embargo.*

was sung about ships carrying contraband.

The compactness of this shanty and its phrasing made it an ideal song for jobs demanding quick tugs on the rope repeated at short intervals.

2

How do you know she's a Yankee liner?
Blow, boys, blow!
The Stars and Stripes float out behind her.
Blow, my bully boys, blow!

3

And who d'you think is the captain of her?
Blow, boys, blow!
Why, Bully Hayes is the captain of her.
Blow, my bully boys, blow!

4

Oh, Bully Hayes, he loves us sailors.
Blow, boys, blow!
Yes, he does, like hell and blazes.
Blow, my bully boys, blow!

Blow, Boys, Blow

*Arrangement
by Elie Siegmeister*

A Yan-kee ship came down the riv - er, Blow, boys, blow! Her
masts and yards they shone like sil - ver. Blow, my bul-ly boys, blow!

5

And what do you think they've got for dinner?
Blow, boys, blow!
Pickled eels' feet and bullock's liver.
Blow, my bully boys, blow!

6

Blow, boys, blow, the sun's drawing water.
Blow, boys, blow!
Three cheers for the cook and one for his daughter.
Blow, my bully boys, blow!

BLOW THE MAN DOWN

"BLOW THE MAN DOWN" tells of the unfortunate adventures of many a sailor boy who found himself shanghaied aboard a ship with a tough-boned skipper as the result of the charms of a fair damsel. Speaking of its origin, Eloise Linscott * says:

* Eloise Linscott: "Folk Songs of Old New England."

". . . . from the port of Liverpool, England, we have this most famous halyard chantey of the Atlantic packet ships. The earliest version of this song the Black Ball line, which began its maritime service in 1818. The scorn with which the Shanteymen looked upon these Western Ocean packets and the crews that manned them is vividly expressed here:

> *And when those packets were ready for sea,*
> *You'd split your sides laughing such sights you'd see,*
> *There were tinkers and tailors and soldiers as well,*
> *All shipped as sailors on board the Blue Bell.*

"The melody has remained the same through years of transition. 'Blow' as used here by the sailor means 'knock'. The street named in the song varies. The Winchester Street of some versions was the section where persons of rank lived; Paradise Street is said to have been a disreputable section along the waterfront."

2

As I was a-walking down Paradise Street,
To me way, aye, blow the man down.
A pretty young damsel I chanced for to meet
Give me some time to blow the man down!

3

She was round in the counter and bluff in bow,
To me way, aye, blow the man down.
So I took in all sail and cried, "Way enough now!"
Give me some time to blow the man down!

4

I hailed her in English, she answered me clear,
To me way, aye, blow the man down.
"I'm from the *Black Arrow* bound to the *Shakespeare.*"
Give me some time to blow the man down!

5

So I tailed her my flipper and took her in tow,
To me way, aye, blow the man down.
And yardarm to yardarm away we did go,
Give me some time to blow the man down!

6

But as we were going she said unto me,
To me way aye, blow the man down.
"There's a spanking full-rigger just ready for sea."
Give me some time to blow the man down!

7

That spanking full rigger to New York was bound,
To me way aye, blow the man down.
She was very well manned and very well found,
Give me some time to blow the man down!

8

But soon as that packet was clear of the bar,
To me way aye, blow the man down.
The mate knocked me down with the end of a spar,
Give me some time to blow the man down!

9

And as soon as that packet was out on the sea,
To me way aye, blow the man down.
'Twas devilish hard treatment of every degree,
Give me some time to blow the man down!

Blow the Man Down

*Arrangement
by Elie Siegmeister*

10

So I give you fair warning before we belay;
To me way aye, blow the man down.
Don't ever take heed of what pretty girls say,
Give me some time to blow the man down!

The Boston Come-All-Ye

Arrangement
by Elie Siegmeister

Come all ye young sail-or men, list-en to me, I'll sing you a song of the fish of the sea. Then blow ye winds west-er-ly, west-er-ly blow, We're bound to the south-'ard, so stead-y she goes.

2

Oh, first come the shale, the biggest of all,
He clumb up aloft and let ev'ry sail fall.
CHORUS: Then blow, *etc.*

3

And next come the mack'rel with his striped back,
He hauled aft the sheets and boarded each tack.
CHORUS: Then blow, *etc.*

THE BOSTON COME-ALL-YE

A WIDELY POPULAR fo'c'sle song in which the sailor boy imagines what the fish would say if they could talk. Here the herring, the mackerel, the codfish express their views on life.

4
Then come the porpoise with his short snout,
He went to the wheel crying, "Ready! About!"
CHORUS: Then blow, *etc.*

5
Then come the smelt, the smallest of all,
He jumped to the poop, and sung out, "Topsail haul!"
CHORUS: Then blow, *etc.*

6
The herring come saying, "I'm king of the seas,
If you want any wind, why I'll blow you a breeze."
CHORUS: Then blow, *etc.*

7
Next came the cod with his chuckle-head;
He went to the main-chains to heave at the lead.
CHORUS: Then blow, *etc.*

8
Last came the flounder as flat as the ground,
Says, "Damn your eyes, chuckle-head, mind how you sound!"
CHORUS: Then blow, *etc.*

Lowlands

Arrangement by Elie Siegmeister

broad

Low- lands, low- lands, a - way, my John

Oh, my old moth-er, she wrote to me, My dol-lar and a half a

day; She wrote to me to come back from sea.

Lowlands, lowlands, away, my John.
A dollar and a half is a black man's pay,
My dollar and a half a day;
Five dollars a day is a white man's pay.

86

LOWLANDS

"LOWLANDS" is one of the most beautiful of shantys. It is a curious compound of a refrain of an old English ballad and an interpretation by negro sailors out of Mobile. Americans and British shipped indiscriminately on vessels of both countries wherever the job was to be had that would take them off the beach. And this intermixture has made it impossible to say whether any given shanty is of American or English origin. The melodic line has a long sweep, and the modal harmonies are intended to suggest a vast expanse of rolling ocean.

SHENANDOAH

"SHENANDOAH" was an early land ballad about a trader who wooed the daughter of an Indian chief and then left her on the shores of the wide Missouri. The song was taken to sea, possibly by some of those roving lumberjacks who worked in the woods in winter and aboard ship during the summer. Without serious alterations, it became one of the most famous and widely sung of American shantys. It is that rare phenomenon, a slow, almost unrhythmical shanty.

Shenandoah

*Arrangement
by Elie Siegmeister*

Oh, Shen-an-doah, I long to hear you A-way, my rol-ling riv-er! Oh, Shen-an-doah, I can't get near you. A-way, a-way, I'm bound a-way, 'Cross the wide Mis-sour-i!

2
Oh, Shenandoah, I love your daughter.
Away, my rolling river!
She lives across the stormy water.
Away, away, I'm bound away,
'Cross the wide Missouri!

3
She said she would not be my lover.
Away, my rolling river!
Because I was a dirty sailor.
Away, away, I'm bound away,
'Cross the wide Missouri!

A Dollar and a Half a Day

Arrangement
by Elie Siegmeister

Five dol-lars a day is a white man's pay, way —
Five dol lars a day is a white man's pay. My dol-lar and a half a day.

2

But a dollar and a half is a black man's pay, way—
But a dollar and a half is a black man's pay,
My dollar and a half a day.

Rio Grande

Arrangement
by Elie Siegmeister

90

pret-ty young girls, For we're bound to the Ri - o Grande!

RIO GRANDE

DURING THE MEXICAN WAR, Yankee ships sailed every ocean, some court-ing adventure by delivering contraband below the Rio Grande. This capstan shanty grew up in those days and has been popular ever since.

2

Oh, say, were you ever in Rio Grande?
Way, you Rio!
It's there that the river runs down golden sand.
For we're bound to the Rio Grande!

CHORUS: And away, *etc.*

3

Oh, New York town is no place for me—
Way, you Rio!
I'll pack up my bag and go to sea.
For we're bound to the Rio Grande!

CHORUS: And away, *etc.*

4

Now, you Bowery ladies, we'll let you know,
Way, you Rio!
We're bound to the South'ard, O Lord, let her go!
For we're bound to the Rio Grande!

CHORUS: And away, *etc.*

5

We'll sell our salt cod for molasses and rum—
Way, you Rio!
And get home again 'fore Thanksgiving has come.
For we're bound to the Rio Grande!

CHORUS: And away, *etc.*

4. Ho, Boys, Ho

AFTER THE REVOLUTION, and particularly after the War of 1812, the young country radiated enthusiasm and energy. A small upstart of a nation, it had just licked the greatest empire in the world and was ready for new adventures. It was expanding in all directions at once, sending its clippers out over the high seas and its population out into the uncharted land of the West. Footloose adventurers, farmers who had heard of fertile land to be had for the asking, immigrants from the troubled nations of the outside world, started out in whatever conveyance they could obtain. The stream of immigration, which had been steadily flowing since the War of Independence, now became a veritable torrent. Over mountains, on rivers, on foot, on horseback, in wagons, pushing carts before them, in river boats, whole families pulled up their stakes and set out for the Promised Land stretching before them in never-ending expanse.

Between 1770 and 1840 the westward movement grew from a handful of people to hundreds of thousands. Millions of acres were occupied by the moving hordes. McMaster tells us "reports from Lancaster (Pa.) state that 100 moving families had been counted going through the town *in a week,* and that the turnpike was fairly covered with bands of immigrants. At Zanesville (Ohio) 50 wagons crossed the Muskingum in one day." In spite of tremendous difficulties—roads that were quagmires, rivers that were often floods, attacks by the Indians—the settlers moved steadily on through the passes of Pennsylvania into the Ohio Valley, up through Ohio, Indiana, and Illinois, and down over the Cumberland Gap through Kentucky and Tennessee.

Davy Crockett is reported to have said to his wife one day, "There's some new settlers ten miles down the valley and I feel kind of crowded, so let's pull up and move on." Rarely did they stay put in the Promised Land; always there were new and better horizons farther on, new land for better herding, more fertile fields, less crowding. Abraham Lincoln's family went from Pennsylvania to Kentucky, where he was born in 1809. Seven years later they got on a raft and moved down the Ohio to Indiana. Fourteen years after that, his family moved again to Illinois. This was the rhythm of frontier life.

It was inevitable that this life in a wilderness, with its innumerable hardships and dangers, should develop a new type of man. He was energetic, hard-working, boastful and fearless. He was plain, disliked show or snobbishness, and since all he owned he had built with his own hands, he had a fundamental belief in himself and did not feel like taking orders from anyone.

It is plain to see that every aspect of this migration and this establishment of a new kind of life lent itself to the creation of song. Men on expeditions and men in danger, men on lonely frontiers and men in dark forests, sing. They sing for courage, for cheer and companionship, out of pride, out of sheer boisterousness. Women who care for children alone in the heart of the wilderness, with neighbors many miles off, croon their own lullabies and create their own work songs. Singing was one of the chief forms of recreation on the frontier. There were no theatres, no social gatherings, no time for such frippery. Men couldn't play cards, with the nearest neighbor twenty-five miles away, but people had their own voices and the treasury of song that they had brought along in their own memories. There must have been hosts of songs reflecting these early pioneer days, but few of them were recorded because people had no time or thought to give to such a thing as writing down music.

So the songs that have come down to us have arrived mainly by accident or because they persisted in other forms. The old song, for example:

> Come all ye fine young fellows
> Who have got a mind to range
> Into some far-off countree
> Your fortune for to change.
> We'll lay us down upon the banks
> Of the blessed O-hi-o,
> Through the wild woods we'll wander
> And chase the buffalo.

would have been entirely forgotten had it not been taken up and made over into a play-party song, called "Shoot the Buffalo," in which form it is still sung today. Many songs were translated into spirituals and thus were recorded.

However, we still have a few of the original songs as they were sung in those days. They were the songs of the bullwhackers who drove the wagons, or the legends of the early *voyageurs* or fur traders, and the later professional boatmen who ferried the immigrants down the Ohio, Muskingum, and a dozen other streams, songs of early land boom experts and of lads and girls who were going off over the mountains in search of some faithless lover.

The pioneer songs that did get recorded were the religious songs and ballads. Musically, these were very little if at all, different from the folk songs. There was no established church on the frontier, no regular services, no fixed hymns. What religion there was came from the family Bible, which was always at hand, together with the rifle and axe, and from the circuit riding preachers, who, though in many cases not ordained by theological schools, yet felt the call of God strongly enough to brave hunger, thirst, Indians, wild animals, and the sometimes still wilder frontiersmen, to bring the Gospel into the very heart of the wilderness. Along with other ballads, frontiersmen would remember a few lines from some old hymn. With no set books to make them toe the mark,

these, with the addition of other phrases that would come to mind were soon fused and a new religious ballad or spiritual was born. Tunes flowed back and forth between the profane and religious ballads with the greatest of ease. The pioneers saw nothing incongruous in this, and indeed such a process has been going on ever since religion first started.

Or a spiritual might spring up this way: A circuit riding preacher during his long journey on horseback from one settlement to another, had plenty of time to think of what sermon he would preach and what hymn he would sing at the next meeting, which might be hundreds of miles off. Looking at the wilderness around him, what would be more natural than to take the forest, the trees, the skies, the presence of God in nature, as his theme? If he were apt at making verses, and many of them were, he might take some well-known tune as a starting point and fit religious words to it on this theme. At the next point of call, instead of singing the Doxology, he might sing his new hymn, and if it took, the frontiersman or his wife might go away humming it.

"Through All the World," "Poor Wayfaring Stranger" and "When Adam Was Created" are among the hundreds of spirituals which probably originated in some such manner. In many cases, of course, the pioneer himself, if he was a God-fearing man—and most of them were—might create such a religious song all on his own, without the help of any preacher, as a means of serving the Lord.

But perhaps the largest number of these songs grew up in that characteristic American institution, the camp meeting, which was a regular feature of frontier life. The announcement that a revival meeting was to be held generally would provoke tense excitement, for it was not only a religious gathering, but a social one as well, a chance to see his friends, trade, and later even go on drinking parties and hold games and contests of all sorts. Crowds would flock to the revival from miles around, and as the preacher delivered his sermon, which was usually burning with hell-fire and brimstone, the reactions of the mixed congregation were by no means demure. The listeners would shout, jump around, roll on the ground, scream with laughter and tears, fall into uncontrollable spasms and jerks, and into spontaneous singing. Needless to say, many of these songs were gibberish, but under the pressure of the exciting experience others developed a highly stimulating drive and lift. They were generally made up out of familiar phrases from the Scriptures, interspersed with hallelujahs, refrains of familiar songs, and phrases of common speech. When someone would strike up a refrain such as "We are bound for the Promised Land," the whole crowd would pile in with a roar that would make the wilderness shake.

Camp meetings songs had to be so simple that everyone, young and old alike, without any previous learning, could join in and be carried along. It is not surprising that we find familiar lines cropping up in one song after another, such as "I am bound for glory," "Say, brothers, will you join me?" "Shout Salvation, brothers," etc.

The verse was often given out by the leader, the crowd joining in only on the well-known refrain. It was at such camp meetings—and there were tens of thousands of them—that songs like the "Promised Land," reflecting the optimism of a growing America and of a country just opening up, were born. Many of the texts reflect the actual surroundings of the western frontier. Thus love of the new land is mirrored in "Whitestown"

> *Where nothing dwelt but beasts of prey*
> *Or men as fierce and wild as they,*
> *He bids th' oppress'd and poor repair,*
> *And build them towns and cities there.*
> *They sow the fields, and trees they plant,*
> *Whose yearly fruit supplies their want;*
> *Their race grows up from fruitful stocks,*
> *Their wealth increases with their flocks.*

The spiritual, "War Department," no doubt followed the close of one of the perennial Indian wars:

> *No more shall the sound of the war-whoops*
> *be heard,*
> *The ambush and slaughter no longer be*
> *fear'd.*
> *The tomahawk buried, shall rest in the*
> *ground,*
> *And peace and good-will to the nations*
> *abound.*

And "Liberty" expressed pithily the frontiersmen's most characteristic feeling:

> *No more beneath th' oppressive hand*
> *Of tyranny we mourn,*
> *Behold the smiling, happy land,*
> *That freedom calls her own.*

Were it not for the existence of the early singing-school teachers on the frontier, none of this music would have come down to us. They were professional musicians who followed the circuit preachers, generally in the slightly more settled regions, and earned their way by organizing religious singing semesters in the tradition of the early New England singing schools.

Singing schools of this type existed in western Tennessee and Kentucky more than a hundred years ago. Since the local teachers had to deal with untutored pupils, they simplified the difficult task of reading from music by using the old New England system of notation in which the shape of the notes indicated the pitch, even though the reader might know nothing of the lines and spaces of the clef.

Many of the early singing masters made their own, sometimes crude, but often distinctly original arrangements of well-known songs and published their own books. They were thus able to serve the Lord and realize an excellent profit as well. Mr. Billy Walker, A. S. H. (Author of the "Southern Harmony"—he said he would rather have the letters "A.S.H." after his name than the word "Pres." before it) sold over 600,000 copies of his book in the mid-west, an area most people would consider "that great musical desert." Collections such as "The Sacred Harp" have gone into many editions and are still used in these districts. Many of the songs have a distinct and powerful effect when sung, even though they look curious on paper. They have unusual harmonies which are often strange to the modern ear, and they violate conventional rules quite as radically as modern compositions. The spirituals in these songsters were home-grown and bred in the open air, and they take on a decidedly regional and distinctive American country style. "Singing Billy" Walker, and many other native country composers continued the tradition of William Billings' fuguing tunes. Though it seems incredible, these rather intricate pieces were actually sung by the raw pioneers, and if we are to believe George P. Jackson, they are still performed at the "Big Singings" in the South today. He tells us * that even youngsters in their teens can hold a part in these by no means simple contrapuntal pieces.

Another characteristic development of frontier life was the play-party song. Play parties were simply games played to the accompaniment of singing, varying all the way from simple steps like "Going to Jerusalem" and "Here Come Three Dukes A-riding," still played by children today, to intricate dance steps complete with calls, formations and turns, to such tunes as "Weevily Wheat," "Old Joe Clark," and Old Dan Tucker," very much like the square dances of today.

But it would never do to call them "dances." That would be sinful and the pioneers were a God-fearing people. Many a young bucko and his girl were haled before meeting charged with "dancing to devil-tunes." Since Puritan days, devil tunes were simply those played on a fiddle, banjo, or some other instrument. And to this day there are thousands in Oklahoma, Missouri and elsewhere who would not think of stepping out on a floor when a fiddle is playing. But so long as the music is merely their own singing, they will "play games," doing the same dance steps to the very same tunes from early evening to early morning.

In early days, play parties were an ideal means of solving the entertainment problem in

* G. P. Jackson: "White Spirituals in the Southern Uplands."

the simplest way available. In sparsely settled regions they gave people an opportunity to meet and enjoy themselves, and the frontier people held one on every possible occasion. When a new settler arrived, the word would go around, and men would come together from miles around to help with the house-raising The weight of the logs made this a task requiring the combined efforts of a large crew, and this help was always cheerfully forthcoming. Corn huskings, log rollings, apple and pumpkin cuttings were other jobs that brought folk together. The women would make use of the opportunity for quilting, sewing, spinning thread, and preparing the community feast or barbecue, which always followed such gatherings. A play party was always sure to round out the evening. Several hours of singing and "playing" would generally wind up in drinking bouts for the married men and "sparking" for the younger folk.

What kind of music was sung at these parties? The tunes might be taken from anywhere and everywhere: old ballads, children's songs, wagon tunes, square dances, and at a later date, minstrel songs from the cities, army songs, and whatnot. But when sung at a play party, they all took on a characteristic lively swing, irresistibly gay and infectious, and full of the movement of sturdy legs and bodies. As memories were often short, and the evenings long, old verses got new twists and new ones were improvised on the spur of the moment. It was fun to sing out an unexpected new rhyme, and as the hour grew later, the sallies would often become more pointed and reckless.

> Take her by the lily-white hand
> And lead her like a pigeon.
> Make her dance to 'Weevily Wheat'
> And scatter her religion.

Some of the tunes furnish an ideal framework for new verses. "Skip to My Lou" is sung in 160 different versions in Oklahoma alone. Sometimes queer changes take place. "Weevily Wheat," which began its career hundreds of years ago with verses about bonnie Prince Charlie, now is sung to words about trading boats which serve the Southern plantations. Along with much nonsense, triviality and sheer fun, the songs reflect the migrations and the new environments, even in their titles: "Pig in the Parlor," "Way Down in the Paw Paw," "Hog Drovers Are We," "Shoot the Buffalo." They reflect an exuberant simplicity and joy in life that have kept them a living part of America even today.

Star of Columbia

Words by Dr. Dwight
Music attributed to Miss M. T. Durham

*Arrangement
by Elie Siegmeister*

Co - lum - bia, Co - lum - bia, to glor - y a - rise, The queen of the

world and the child of the skies, Thy gen - ius com - mands thee, with

rap - tures be - hold, While age - s on age - s thy splen - dors un - fold.

Thy reign is the last and the nobl - est of time, Most fruit - ful thy

soil, most in - vit - ing thy clime, Let crimes of the east ne'er en-

crim - son thy name, Be free - dom and sci - ence and vir-tue thy fame.

STAR OF COLUMBIA

"A RISING NATION, spread over a wide and fruitful land, traversing all seas, with the rich productions of their industry, engaged in commerce with nations who feel power and forget rights, advancing rapidly to destinies beyond the reach of mortal eye. When I contemplate these objects, I shrink from the contemplation and shrink from the magnitude of the undertaking."

Jefferson's Inaugural Address.

THIS SONG which may have already been current during Jefferson's presidency, radiates the energy of a young nation in its 'teens. The melody has the wildness and fierceness which, together with its marked pentatonic flavor, lead one to suspect that it might well be a descendant of those old Scotch war songs brought into the Appalachians by the Highlanders. The present harmonization, in open fourths and fifths, based on that made in 1835 by Billy Walker, emphasizes the rugged quality of the text.

2

To conquest and slaughter let Europe aspire,
'Whelm nations in blood, or wrap cities in fire;
Thy heroes the rights of mankind shall defend,
And triumph pursue them and glory attend.

A world is thy realm, for a world be thy laws,
Enlarged as thy empire, and just as thy cause;
On freedom's broad basis that empire shall rise,
Extend with the main and dissolve with the skies.

The Unconstant Lover

*Arrangement
by Elie Siegmeister*

O come, all my young lov-ers, Whom-so-ev-er wants to gao, An' we'll all set-tle daown On the O- hi- o.

<table>
<tr><td>

2

An' we'll chaw aour terbacker,
An' smeoke aour pipes,
An' eat aour pertaties,
Whensoever they gits ripe.

</td><td>

3

Naow a meetin' are a pleasure,
An' a partin' are a grief;
But an unconstant lover
Is wusser nor a thief.

</td></tr>
</table>

4

'Cos a thief he will rob ye
Of all thet you have;
But an unconstant lover
Will tote ye to yer grave!

When Adam Was Created

*Arrangement
by Elie Siegmeister*

When A - dam was cre - a - ted, he dwelt in E - den's shade, As

Mo - ses has re - la - ted, be - fore a bride was made; Ten

thou - sand times ten thou - sand of crea - tures swarmed a - round, Be -

fore a bride was form ed or a ny mate was found.

WHEN ADAM WAS CREATED

A MARRIAGE SERMON in song, this early white spiritual cites the Biblical story of the first couple to be joined in wedlock as the model of marital conduct for all generations. The homely counsel has been preached for the last hundred years in the tones of a simple modal melody.

2

He had no consolation, but seemed as one alone,
Till, to his admiration, he found he'd lost a bone.
This woman was not taken from Adam's head, we know;
And she must not rule o'er him, 'tis evidently so.

3

This woman she was taken from under Adam's arm;
And she must be protected from injury and harm.
This woman was not taken from Adam's feet, we see;
And she must not be abused, the meaning seems to be.

4

This woman she was taken from near to Adam's heart,
By which we are directed that they should never part.
The book that's called the Bible, be sure you don't neglect,
For in every sense of duty, it will you both direct.

5

To you, most loving bridegroom; to you, most loving bride,
Be sure you live a Christian and for your house provide.
Avoiding all discontent, don't sow the seed of strife,
As is the solemn duty of every man and wife.

The Promised Land

Words: Traditional
Music attributed to Miss M. Durham

Arrangement
by Elie Siegmeister

On Jor - dan's storm - y banks I stand, And cast a wish - ful eye, To Can - aan's fair and hap - py land, Where my pos - ses - sions lie. I am bound for the prom - ised land, bound for the prom - ised land Oh, who will come and go with me? I am bound for the prom - ised land.

THE PROMISED LAND

To THE early pioneer, the phrase, "the promised land" referred not only to the Heavenly pastures that lay beyond death, but also to the fertile earth that stretched beyond the Alleghanies. It was a phrase that recurred in conversation, in diaries, in letters written home. It was natural that it should spring up time and again in a score of camp meeting songs and spirituals. When the faithful sang of Heaven with its "sweet fields arrayed in living green" and its "wide extended plains" it was from the landscapes of Ohio, Indiana and Illinois that they borrowed their imagery.

The rhythm of this spirited refrain sounded in many a wilderness camp-meeting during the "Great Southern and Western Revival" of the early nineteenth century.

2

There generous fruits that never fail
On trees immortal grow;
There rocks and hills and brooks and vales
With milk and honey flow.

CHORUS: I am bound, etc.

4

No chilling winds nor poisonous breath
Can reach that healthful shore;
Sickness and sorrow, pain and death
Are felt and feared no more.

CHORUS: I am bound, etc.

3

O, the transporting rapt'rous scene
That rises to my sight,
Sweet fields arrayed in living green
And rivers of delight.

CHORUS: I am bound, etc.

5

All o'er those wide extended plains
Shines one eternal day;
There God the Son forever reigns,
And scatters night away.

CHORUS: I am bound, etc.

6

When shall I reach that happy place,
And be forever blest?
When shall I see my Father's face,
And in his bosom rest?

CHORUS: I am bound, etc.

Weevily Wheat

Arrangement
by Elie Siegmeister

I don't want none of your weev i ly wheat, I don't want none of your bar - ley, I want some flour and half an hour To bake a cake for Char - lie.

2

Charlie he's a fine young man,
Charlie he's a dandy;
He loves to hug and kiss the girls
And feed 'em on good candy.

3

The higher up the cherry tree,
The riper grows the cherry;
The more you hug and kiss the girls,
The sooner they will marry.

WEEVILY WHEAT

THE FEET of early New England settlers trod a lively measure to the sung verses of this play-party song. In the early eighteen hundreds pioneers danced to it in the maple swamps of Indiana, "where the water's deep and muddy." It reached the Southern plantations, where a verse about the "trading boats" that carried away the cotton was added. It was finally taken westward. There young folk still sing and "play" to verses about weevily wheat and barley.

4

Take her by the lily white hand,
And lead her like a pigeon,
Make her dance to "Weevily Wheat,"
And scatter her religion.

5

Trading boats have gone ashore,
Trading boats are landing;
Trading boats have gone ashore
Loaded down with candy.

6

'Way down yonder in the maple swamp,
Where the water's deep and muddy,
We'll dance and sing till broad daylight,
And won't get home till Sunday.

7

If you love me like I love you,
We'll have no time to tarry,
We'll have the old folks flying around,
Fixing for us to marry.

8

I have got a sweet little wife,
A wife of my own choosing;
Hug her neat and kiss her sweet
And go no more a-courting.

Shoot the Buffalo

Arrangement
by Elie Siegmeister

Rise you up, my dear-est dear, And pre-sent to me your hand, And we'll all run a-way To some far and dis-tant land, Where the la-dies knit and sew, And the gents they plow and hoe, And we'll ram-ble in the cane-brake And shoot the buf-fa-lo.

SHOOT THE BUFFALO

IN THE early nineteenth century there was a pioneer ballad, "Hunt the Buffalo," which invited footloose young men into the wildwoods to chase the hump-backed beast which apparently still ranged the banks of the "O-hi-o." Shortly afterward, some of the lines of this ballad were incorporated in a play-party song.

The buffalo has long since vanished not only from the shores of the Ohio, but even from the western plains, and with it "Hunt the Buffalo" disappeared. But youngsters in Oklahoma, Texas and Missouri still dance on Saturday nights as they sing to their young ladies to accompany them to "some fair and distant land" where they can "ramble through the canebreak and shoot the buffalo."

2

Rise you up, my dearest dear,
And present to me your paw,
I'm sure you've got terbacker,
I'd like to have a chaw.

Oh, the rabbit shot the monkey
And the monkey shot the crow,
Let us ramble in the cane-break
And shoot the buffalo.

3

Where the women sit and patch
And the men stand and scratch,
We'll all meet together
In the old potato patch.

All the way from Georgia
To Texas I must go
To rally 'round the cane-brake
And shoot the buffalo.

additional verses to "Shoot the Buffalo"

Come all ye fine young fellows
Who have got a mind to range
Into some far off countree
Your fortune for to change.
We'll lay us down upon the banks
Of the blessed O-hi-o;
Through the wildwoods we'll wander,
And we'll chase the buffalo.

2

Come all ye fine young women
Who have got a mind to go,
That you may make us clothing
You can knit and you can sew.
We'll build you fine log cabins
By the blessed O-hi-o;
Through the wildwoods we'll wander,
And we'll chase the buffalo.

3

And should the dread wild Indians
By chance to us come near,
We'll all unite together,
And show we have no fear.
We'll bind ourselves together
And strike the fatal blow;
Through the wildwoods we'll wander,
And we'll chase the buffalo.

Skip to My Lou

Arrangement by Elie Siegmeister

SKIP TO MY LOU

"THE PLAY PARTY is a development of frontier life. . . . The square dance, to which the early settlers would have turned was often impossible because of lack of music. In the earliest settlements along the frontier, pianos and organs were unheard of, and violins were almost as rare. . . . Jigs and pigeon wings were frequently danced to the staccato rhythm of bones rattled by skilled hands or thimbled fingers on a tin washboard. But community dancing could not be had to such accompaniment, and as a result, the people turned to singing their simple directions for the dance movements." *

* Owens: Swing and Turn."

2

Gone again, skip to my Lou,
Gone again, skip to my Lou,
Gone again, skip to my Lou,
Skip to my Lou, my darling.

3

Stole my partner, skip to my Lou,
Stole my partner, skip to my Lou,
Stole my partner, skip to my Lou,
Skip to my Lou, my darling.

4

I'll get another one prettier than you,
I'll get another one prettier than you,
I'll get another one prettier than you,
Skip to my Lou, my darling.

5

Chicken on the haystack, shoo, shoo, shoo,
Chicken on the haystack, shoo, shoo, shoo,
Chicken on the haystack, shoo, shoo, shoo,
Skip to my Lou, my darling.

DIRECTIONS FOR DANCING

Balance all, skip to my Lou, etc.

Corners swing, skip to my Lou, etc.

Back to your partners, skip to my Lou, etc.

All promenade, skip to my Lou, etc.

5. Tooth-Ache in His Heel

WHILE PIONEER SONGS, spirituals and play-party tunes were developing in the newly settled country districts of the mid-west, an equally characteristic new form of music was growing up in the cities of the East, a form that was destined to produce America's greatest songster: Stephen Foster.

The minstrel show was an outgrowth of the native minstrel bands of the South. As James Weldon Johnson tells us, these could be found on almost every plantation. They consisted of a group of Negro entertainers, who were apt at cutting capers, playing the "bones" and the banjo, and performing comic songs, dances and impersonations with all the natural ease and vitality that is an organic part of their race.

Professional white comedians started, in the 1820's and '30's, to use the jokes, the "Ethiopian" ditties, the hoe-downs, the pigeon wings, and the other entertainments of these plantation companies. They appeared on the stage in black-face. According to tradition, it was "Daddy" Rice who really started the minstrel vogue which for over sixty years was the chief American form of entertainment, and the ancestor of vaudeville, the tap-dance, the musical comedy and Amos 'n Andy. Rice put on his "Jump Jim Crow" act in Louisville in 1830. The story goes that the comedian had watched a Negro stablehand humming a tune and doing some tricky steps. Borrowing his clothes, he reproduced the act on the stage and did so well that the original Jim Crow grew tired of waiting and came on the stage to demand his suit back. The audience apparently thought this was part of the show and roared with laughter.

Like many stories, this is probably too pat to be true. At any rate, the minstrel vogue grew rapidly. Companies of wise-cracking, fiddle-, bones-, and banjo-playing song and dance men in blackface were formed, such as the Virginia Serenaders, the E. P. Christy Minstrels, Callender's Consolidated Minstrels, and the Ethiopian Serenaders. The new type of entertainment was immediately successful and profitable. Tours were made through all the principal cities and the managers vied with one another, as do the band leaders of today, for new numbers that would "pack them in." The slapstick turns of Sambo, Mr. Bones and the Interlocutor needed the backing of both "hot" and "sweet" tunes, and the characteristic lively, syncopated style and the sentimental "old plantation" style were born. Clever composers and arrangers who understood the popular taste and could turn out appropriate numbers plentifully, often to order, were much in demand.

The minstrel show, which was thus founded on basic, even though generally caricatured, folk origins, and on a sound democratic demand for light entertainment, was really the fore-runner of the tradition of the rag-time, jazz and swing that have made American popular music the best in the world. The men and the songs it produced: Dan Emmett, Stephen Foster, James Bland, E. P. Christy, Cool White; and "Old Dan Tucker," "Old Zip Coon," "Oh Susanna," "My Old Kentucky Home," "Dixie," "Carry Me Back to Old Virginny," were America's first contributions that were popular abroad.

Of course, there were those who scorned the low-brow minstrel songs. A critic of 1858 assures us that:

"Such tunes, although whistled and sung by everybody, are erroneously supposed to have taken a deep hold on the popular mind; . . . the charm is only *skin-deep*; . . . they are hummed and whistled 'for lack of thought'; . . . (they) are not popular in the sense of musically inspiring, but . . . such a melody *breaks out* every now and then, like a morbid irritation of the skin." *

The melody referred to was "Old Folks at Home."

There were others who did not estimate Foster's songs at their true value, including Foster himself. He made a present of his "Oh Susanna" and two other songs to a music publisher, W. C. Peters, who published them as "Songs of the Sable Harmonists" and made $10,000 on them. Foster's name was not even mentioned on the copies.

Many a sigh has been heaved and many a homesick heart has beaten more quickly at the lines of "Swanee River." Yet when it was published, Foster had never been further south than the Ohio. He got the name "Swanee" from his brother, who had found it on the map.

When E. P. Christy, the famous minstrel entrepreneur, asked Foster to write songs for him, the agreement stipulated that Christy's, not Foster's, name was to appear on the first edition as composer. This is a practise which, alas, many another budding young song-writer has been obliged to submit to. Thus we find the following title-page:

MUSIC OF THE

ORIGINAL

CHRISTY

MINSTRELS

The oldest established Band in the United States

As arranged and sung by them with distinguished success

OH SUSANNA

OLD FOLKS AT HOME

With regard to one of his songs, Foster wrote to Christy:

"If you accept my proposition I will make it a point to notify you hereafter when I have a new song and send you the ms. on the same terms. . . . Thus it will become notorious that your band brings out all the new songs. You

* John S. Dwight in the *Journal of Music,* quoted by J. T. Howard in "Our American Music."

can state in the papers that the song was composed expressly for you. . . ."

And again:

"I regret that it is too late to have the name of your band on the title page, but I will endeavor to place it (alone) on future songs, and will cheerfully do anything else in my humble way to advance your interest."

Foster wrote many of his songs to order for Christy.

But, in 1852, six months after "Old Folks at Home" was written, Foster wrote to the bandleader, asking that his name be placed on the title page as composer:

"I find I cannot write at all unless I write for public approbation and get credit for what I write."

Twenty-one years later Oliver Ditson & Co. issued a reprint edition, still crediting words and music to Christy.

THE '49ERS

In a vigorous, thriving civilization, folk songs and professionally composed songs have a close relationship. Much of the energy of the minstrel music came from the strong folk element in it: from the fiddle jigs, banjo strains, plantation tunes of the South, to whose influence even Foster was not impervious. Now the time had come for the current to flow in the other direction, and it did—into the wagon ballads, Cape Horn chanties, and sagas of the Gold Rush. The rush for gold was a great human adventure, to inspire great and crazy songs; a comic and tragic epic of a nation on the loose: something fantastic for a Breughel or a Daumier to paint. Greenbie tells of it:

"When the word flashed over the mountains that this land . . . contained gold—gold in unlimited quantities, gold that could be washed out of the sands, picked out of the rocks with the fingernails—the wildest stampede in history began. Into the West they poured, in wagons, on horseback, on foot. Out of the harbors they dashed, in sailing boats, in steamers, in anything that could keep afloat. The news spread to Europe. The ports of the Atlantic were crammed with immigrants seeking transshipment. It ran down the coast of South America and up the other side, and almost all of Chile set sail at once. It flashed across Canada and the trappers dropped their pelts and beat it down the coast. It flashed from ship to ship in the Orient, and across the Pacific they came flying loaded with everybody from maharajahs to Chinese."

This fantastic migration could not help pouring out into song. Enthusiasts piled into overloaded leaky boats for the long journey around the Horn with song on their lips. Alkali Ike and Joe Bowers tramped over endless miles of desert singing "Ho for California!" to any one of a dozen tunes. Composed songs, popular stage or vaudeville hits, came back to the common folk and were twisted to fit the verses about the "Promised Land." Foster's "Oh Susanna" and "Camp Town Races" were among the most parodied, and they echoed through Rocky Mountain passes to lines of every character.

Another chapter in the annals of American music had been recorded.

Old Dan Tucker

*Words and Music
by Dan Emmett*

*Arrangement
by Elie Siegmeister*

OLD DAN TUCKER

COMPOSED IN 1830 by Dan Emmett, who was later to become the author of "Dixie," this became one of the most famous of all minstrel songs. It soon penetrated into the play-party and square dance country, where it still retains its popularity, long after the minstrel show has been forgotten. When John Steinbeck describes a contemporary Oklahoma square dance, in his "Grapes of Wrath," "Old Dan Tucker" is the tune the fiddler is playing.

S. Foster Damon, in his notes to the "Series of Old American Songs" * says that the chorus of this tune contains the first example of syncopation in blackface song.

"Old Dan Tucker" played an unusual role in an interesting episode of early New York history: the Tin Horn rent war. The farmers of Columbia County had been living in a semi-feudal condition, in which they gave menial service and shared crops with the land-owners, in return for the use of the land. In 1844, led by a Dr. Boughton, they determined to do away with the contracts which bound them. Appearing one night disguised as Indians, wearing calico hats, blowing on tin horns, they sang a song to the tune of "Old Dan Tucker" in which they expressed their feelings about Big Bill Snyder, the sheriff of the County who was responsible for enforcing the oppressive regulations. Snyder was forced to hand over the contracts, and two years later a new State Constitution was adopted which abolished feudal services forever in the Hudson Valley.

* S. Foster Damon: Brown University Series of Old American Songs.

2

Old Daniel Tucker was a mighty man,
He washed his face in a frying pan,
Combed his head wid a wagon wheel,
An' died wid de toothache in his heel.
CHORUS: So, git out, *etc.*

3

Old Dan Tucker's back in town,
Swingin' the ladies all aroun';
First to the right and then to the left,
An' then to the gal that he loves best.
CHORUS: So, git out, *etc.*

4

Old Dan Tucker's mother-in-law,
Was the ugliest thing I ever saw,
Her eyes stuck out an' her nose stuck in,
Her upper lip hung over her chin.
CHORUS: So, git out, *etc.*

5

Old Dan Tucker he got drunk,
He fell in de fire an' he kicked up a chunk;
De red hot coals got in his shoe
An' whee-wee! how de ashes flew!
CHORUS: So, git out, *etc.*

You're too late to come to sup - per.

6	7
I went to meetin' de udder day,	Tucker is a nice old man,
To hear old Tucker preach an' pray,	He us'd to ride our darby ram,
Dey all got drunk, but me alone,	He sent him whizzin' down de hill,
I make ole Tucker walk-jaw-bone.	If he hadn't got up, he'd laid dar still.
CHORUS: So, git out, *etc.*	

OLD DAN TUCKER
(*Down Rent Verses*)

The moon was shining silver bright,
The sheriff came at dead of night
High on a hill an Indian true
And on his horn a blast he blew.

CHORUS:
Get out the way, Big Bill Snyder,
Get out the way, Big Bill Snyder,
Get out the way, Big Bill Snyder,
We'll tar your coat and feather your hide, sir.

2

Bill thought he heard the sound of a gun
He cried in fright, "O my race is run,
Better that I'd never been born
Than come within sound of that big horn."
CHORUS: Get out the way, *etc.*

Lubly Fan

Words and Music by Cool White

As I was lumb-'ring down de street, Down de street, down de street, A pret-ty gal I chanc'd to meet, O she was fair to view. Den lub-ly Fan will you cum out to-night, Will you cum out to-night, will yo

cum out to night, Den - lub ly Fan will you cum out to - night, An'

dance by de lite ob de moon.

LUBLY FAN

ANOTHER PERENNIAL minstrel favorite, this one took on a number of pseudonyms early in its career. In 1844 a black-face comedian brought the song closer to home in New York by singing, "Bowery gals" instead of "Lubly Fan, won't you come out to-night?" This practice was adopted by other minstrels on tour, and that is how the song became known as "Buffalo Gals," "Louisiana Gals," "Pittsburgh Gals."

The printed accompaniments to minstrel songs, like the sheet music versions of present day jazz, were far simpler than the music used in actual performance.

2

I stopt her an' I had some talk
Had some talk, had some talk,
But her foot covered up de whole side-walk
An' left no room for me.

CHORUS: Den lubly Fan, *etc.*

3

She's de prettiest gal Ibe seen in my life,
Seen in my life, seen in my life,
An' I wish to de Lord she was my wife,
Den we would part no more.

CHORUS: Den lubly Fan, *etc.*

4

Oh make haste, Fan, don't make me wait,
Make me wait, make me wait,
I fear you've kept me now too late,
Yes, dere's de ebening gun.

CHORUS: Den lubly Fan, *etc.*

Old Zip Coon

Words and Music attributed to
Bob Farrell

Arrangement
by Elie Siegmeister

coon-y in a holler   Pos-sum up a gum tree,   coon-y on a stump

Pos   sum   up   a   gum   tree,   coon-y   on   a   stump

Pos-sum   up   a   gum   tree,   coon-y   on   a   stump   Den

o-ver dub-ble trub——ble,——   Zip   Coon   will   jump.

Fiddle Variations - Fast

OLD ZIP COON
(*Turkey in the Straw*)

KNOWN TODAY as the classic American square dance tune, this song won its spurs in the days of Andrew Jackson as a burnt-cork melody. It was first sung by Bob Farrell in the Bowery Theatre, New York, on August 11, 1834, and was quickly spread throughout the country by travelling minstrel companies, who, like the dance bands of today, were quick to pick up the latest New York hits.

If any proof were needed of the deep hold its rakish line and perky rhythms have taken of the American mind, it would be the almost endless string of lyrics which have been fitted to this tune. Besides "Zip Coon" and "Turkey in the Straw" there are "My Grandmother Lived" (said to be of Irish origin) ; "There Was an Old Soldier," which dates from Civil War times; and "There Was a Little Hen," which dates from any drinking party after 2 A. M.

Besides its many offspring, this most American of all tunes also has relatives, perhaps ancestors, abroad. Among those with which it is still on speaking terms are the English "Haymaker's Dance" and the Irish "Rose Tree in Full Bearing."

2

O it's old Suky blue skin, she is in lub wid me,
I went the udder arternoon to take a dish ob tea;
What do you tink now, Suky hab for supper,
Why chicken foot an possum heel, widout any butter.

3

Did you eber see the wild goose, sailing on de ocean,
O de wild goose motion is a bery pretty notion;
Ebry time de wild goose beckens to de swaller,
You hear him google google google google goller.

4

I tell you what will happin den, now bery soon,
De Nited States Bank will be blone to de moon;
Dere General Jackson, will him lampoon,
And de bery nex President, will be Zip Coon.

ANOTHER LITTLE DRINK

Oh, we had an old hen and she had a wooden leg,
And ev'ry morning she used to lay an egg.
She was the best old hen that we had down on the farm,
And another little drink wouldn't do us any harm.

Walk-Jaw-Bone

Words and Music
by S. S. Steele

Arrangement
by Elie Siegmeister

In Car - o - line, whar I was born, I husk de wood, an' I chop de corn, A roast - ed ear to de house I bring, But de driv - er cotch me and he sing: Walk, jaw bone, Jen - ny come a - long, In come Sal - ly wid de boot - ees on; Walk jaw bone,

Jen ny come a - long,   In come Sal- ly wid de   boot - ees on.

WALK-JAW-BONE

As MANY of the minstrel songs were taken directly from Negro folk originals, it is not surprising to find here, beneath the conventional "Ethiopian" clowning and patter, an allegory of slavery and deliverance. In an age when opponents of slavery were hounded, even in the North, the minstrel comedian played the part of the court jester of old. Cavorting about the stage in black-face he could mime the part of the runaway slave and conceal many a stinging thrust in comedy.

One does not usually think of a Polish peasant as the composer of American minstrel tunes. Yet that is exactly what happened in this case, for the melody of "Walk-Jaw-Bone" is note for note that of the Polish folk-dance, "The Krakoviak."

2

De corn de driver from me rob,
An' he make me eat de cob.
I chaw de cob until my gums
Stick out like Carolina plums.
CHORUS: Walk, jaw bone, etc.

4

Dey made me a scar-crow in de field
And a buzzard come to get his meal.
But in his face I blowed my bref
An' he was a case for ole Jim Death.
CHORUS: Walk, jaw bone, etc.

3

Dey fasten me up under de barn
Dey feed me dar on leaves ob corn.
It tickled my digestion so,
Dat I cotch de cholerophoby.
CHORUS: Walk, jaw bone, etc.

5

Den down de bank I see'd a ship,
I slide down dar on de bone ob my hip,
I crossed de brink an' yare I am
If I go back dar, I'll be damn!
CHORUS: Walk, jaw bone, etc.

Alabado

*Arrangement
by Elie Siegmeister*

ALABADO

ONE OF THE FEW remaining Spanish hymns which were brought to the Southwest and taught to the Indians by the missionary priests. When the '49ers came to California, songs like this were chanted in and around the missions. Even as it stands today, changed as it must be by time and memory, it retains the timeless flavor of century-old Gregorian chant.

2

And the pure Conception
Of the Queen of the Heavens
Who, Virgin Immaculate,
Is Mother of Eternal Word.

3

And the blessed Saint Joseph,
Chosen by God the Almighty,
For his reputed Father
Of His Son, the Divine Word.

4

This is for all ages,
And forever. Amen.
Amen. Jesus and Mary:
Jesus, Mary and Joseph.

2

Y la limpia Concepción
De la Reyna los Cielos,
Que quedando Virgen pura,
Es Madre del Verbo Eterno.

3

Y el bendito San José,
Electo por Dios immenso,
Para padre estimativo,
De su Hijo el Divino Verbo.

4

Esto es por todos los siglos,
Y de los siglos, Amen.
Amen, Jesus y Maria:
Jesus, Maria, y José.

Sacramento

Arrangement
by Elie Siegmeister

A bul - ly ship and a bul - ly crew, Doo - da, doo - da! A bul - ly mate and a cap - tain too, Doo - da, doo - da, day! Then blow ye winds, Hi - oh, For Cal - if - or - ny O! There's plent - y of gold, So I've been told, On the banks of Sac - ra - men - to!

SACRAMENTO

WHEN THE NEWS came from Sutter's Creek that there were gold nuggets as big as your fist to be picked up off the ground, the free-for-all rush started. Men packed into leaky sailing boats for the dangerous trip around Cape Horn to San Francisco; later, as Carl Sandburg has pointed out, these ships took thousands of the same passengers back.

Out of this mad Odyssey, a song arose. At first it was sung with enthusiasm. Later, on the return voyages, bitter, sarcastic verses were sung to the same refrain. When the gold-rush fever died down, it remained as a shanty about windjammers and square-riggers.

The similarity of the tune to that of Stephen Foster's "Camp Town Races" written in 1850 is so striking that it is a question which was taken from the other. It is also possible that both derived from the opening lines of the spiritual, "Roll, Jordan, Roll."

Sweet Betsy from Pike

*Arrangement
by Elie Siegmeister*

Did you ever hear tell of sweet, Bet-sy from Pike, Who crossed the wide prair - ies with her lov - er Ike, With two yoke of cat - tle and one spot-ted hog, A tall shang - hai roost - er an old yal - ler dog? Sing too- ral- i- oo- ral- i- oo- ral- i- ay,

SWEET BETSY FROM PIKE

LIFE ABOARD the covered wagons crossing the flats, the Rockies, the alkali desert, was no picnic. Songs serious, comic and grotesque enlivened many miles of endless monotony. This one relates the misfortunes of Ike and his Pike County Rose with sardonic undertones. Disappointed prospectors had at least one outlet: they could laugh at themselves and roar 'Too-ral-i-oo-ral-i-oo-ral-i-ay" for all the prairies to hear.

Never was exquisite sentiment couched in more delicate language than:

"Good-bye, you big lummox, I'm glad you backed out."

2

One evening quite early they camped on the Platte,
'Twas near by the road on a green shady flat;
Where Betsy, quite tired, lay down to repose,
While with wonder Ike gazed on his Pike County rose.

CHORUS: Sing-too-ral, *etc.*

3

They swam the wide rivers and crossed the tall peaks,
And camped on the prairie for weeks upon weeks.
Starvation and cholera and hard work and slaughter,
They reached California spite of hell and high water.

CHORUS: Sing-too-ral, *etc.*

4

Out on the prairie one bright starry night
They broke the whiskey and Betsy got tight,
She sang and she shouted and danced o'er the plain,
And showed her bare arse to the whole wagon train.

CHORUS: Sing-too-ral, *etc.*

5

The Injuns came down in a wild yelling horde,
And Betsy was skeered they would scalp her adored;
Behind the front wagon wheel Betsy did crawl,
And there she fought the Injuns with musket and ball.

CHORUS: Sing-too-ral, *etc.*

6

The alkali desert was burning and bare,
And Isaac's soul shrank from the death that lurked there:
"Dear old Pike County, I'll go back to you."
Says Betsy, "You'll go by yourself if you do."

CHORUS: Sing-too-ral, *etc.*

Joe Bowers

*Arrangement
by Elie Siegmeister*

My name it is Joe Bow - ers, I've got a broth-er Ike, I came from old Mis - sou - ri, all the way from Pike; I'll tell you how it hap - pened I start - ed out to roam, And left my poor old mam-my so far a - way from home.

JOE BOWERS

SUNG IN THE 1850's by bull-whackers and mule drivers following the Gold Rush to California, this was a favorite with Western regiments during the Civil War. They would cheer loudly at the stanza relating that "Sally had a baby and the baby had red hair." It was popular on the vaudeville stage in the '50's and '60's.

2

I used to love a gal thar, they called her Sally Black;
I axed her for to marry me, she said it was a whack;
"But," says she to me, "Joe Bowers, before we hitch for life,
You'd orter have a little home to keep your little wife."

3

Says I, "My dearest Sally, oh, Sally, for your sake,
I'll go to Californy and try to raise a stake."
Says she to me: "Joe Bowers, oh, you are the chap to win.
Give me a kiss to seal the bargin." And she threw a dozen in.

4

I shall ne'er forgit my feelin's when I bid adieu to all.
Sally cotched me round the neck, then I began to bawl.
When I got in they all commenced, you ne'er did hear the like,
How they all took on and cried the day I left old Pike.

5

When I got to this 'ere country, I hadn't nary red;
I had sich wolfish feelin's, I wished myself most dead,
But the thoughts of my dear Sally soon made these feelin's git,
And whispered hopes to Bowers, Lord, I wish I had 'em yit.

6

At length I went to minin', put in my biggest licks,
Come down upon the bowlders jist like a thousand bricks;
I worked both late and early, in rain, and sun and snow,
But I was workin' for my Sally, so 'twas all the same to Joe.

7

I made a very lucky strike, as the gold itself did tell,
And I saved it for my Sally, the gal I loved so well,
I saved it for my Sally, that I might pour it at her feet,
That she might kiss and hug me and call me something sweet.

Oh Susanna!

Chorus

Oh! Su- san - na, Oh! don't you cry for me, I've

come from A - la - ba - ma wid my ban- jo on my knee.

THIS SONG was a money-maker for almost everybody except Stephen Foster. At the time he became twenty-one, he gave a sample copy of "Oh Susanna" to E. P. Christy, the leader of a minstrel show. Christy turned it over to his New York publisher, modestly crediting himself as composer. Later a Louisville publisher, Peters, presented the song, together with "Old Uncle Ned," and made a neat profit of $10,000, while Foster never received a cent.

2

I jumped aboard de telegraph,
And trabbelled down de riber,
De lectric fluid magnified,
And killed five hundred Nigger
De bullgine buste, de horse run off,
I really thought I'd die;
I shut my eyes to hold my breath,
Susanna, don't you cry.
CHORUS:

3

I soon will be in New Orleans,
And den I'll look all round,
And when I find Susanna,
I'll fall upon the ground.
But if I do not find her,
Dis darkie'll surely die,
And when I'm dead and buried,
Susanna, don't you cry.
CHORUS:

My Old Kentucky Home

*Words and Music
by Stephen Foster*

The sun shines bright in the
The young folks roll on the

old Ken - tuck - y home, 'Tis sum - mer, the dark - ies are
lit - tle cab - in floor, All mer - ry, all hap - py, and

gay; The corntop's ripe and the meadow's in the bloom, While the
bright, By'n'by hard times comes a - knocking at the door, Then, my

birds make mu - sic all the day;
old Ken tuck - y home, good-night!

Chorus

Weep no more, my lad - y, Oh! weep no more to - day! We will

sing one song for the old Ken - tuck - y home, For the old Kentuck - y home far a - way.

MY OLD KENTUCKY HOME

THIS SONG, like many other Foster favorites, romanticized the Southern Negro scene. Ironically enough, Foster never visited the South, and received his ideas about Negro life mostly from attending their church services and watching minstrel shows.

Foster's original harmonization is retained.

2.

They hunt no more for the 'possum and the 'coon
On the meadow, the hill, and the shore;
They sing no more by the glimmer of the moon,
On the bench by the old cabin door:
The day goes by like a shadow o'er the heart,
With sorrow where all was delight,
The time has come when the darkies have to part,
Then, my old Kentucky home, good-night!

CHORUS: Weep no more, etc.

3.

The head must bow and the back will have to bend,
Wherever the darky may go;
A few more days and the trouble all will end,
In the fields where the sugar-canes grow;
A few more days for to tote the weary load,
No matter, 'twill never be light,
A few more days till we totter on the road,
Then, my old Kentucky home, good-night!

CHORUS: Weep no more, etc.

Jeanie with the Light Brown Hair

*Words and Music
by Stephen Foster*

*Arrangement
by Elie Siegmeister*

I dream of Jean - ie with the light brown hair, Borne, like a va - por,
on the sum - mer air; I see her trip - ping where the bright streams play,
Hap - py as the dais - ies that dance on her way. Man - y were the wild notes her

mer - ry voice would pour, Man - y were the blithe birds that war - bled them o'er: Oh!_____ I dream of Jean - ie with the light brown hair, Float - ing, like a va - por, on the soft sum - mer air.

JEANIE WITH THE LIGHT BROWN HAIR

A RATHER UNSUCCESSFUL marriage to the daughter of a Pittsburgh physician, a Miss Jane McDowell, was the inspiration for this song. There were periodic separations, and it is quite possible that the song was written in a nostalgic moment when Foster found himself lonesome for her. Whatever its origin, "Jeanie" retains its freshness and charm throughout the years.

2

I long for Jeanie with the day-dawn smile,
Radiant in gladness, warm with winning guile;
I hear her melodies, like joys gone by,
Sighing round my heart o'er the fond hopes that die:—

Sighing like the night wind and sobbing like the rain,—
Wailing for the lost one that comes not again:
Oh! I long for Jeanie, and my heart bows low,
Never more to find her where the bright waters flow.

6. Year of Jubilo

IN THE POPULAR MIND, and therefore in the annals of song in this country, the Civil War, despite various historical interpretations, remains a struggle to end slavery. That is why The Year of Jubilo, or emancipation, was the period close to the minds and hearts of millions of Americans, both black and white.

Although emancipation was for long an unpopular, indeed a dangerous cause to champion, and although it frequently could be spoken of only in whispers, it was inevitable that it would appear in song. The song has always been an outlet for causes and feelings that have been completely frustrated and pent up in other channels.

The Negro himself sang of freedom. At first it was freedom symbolized in religion: "The Great Jubilee" or "Dat Great Day in de Mornin' " or "Kingdom Come." Many of the finest spirituals come from the slave plantations and are expressed in terms of religious symbolism, but, as Frederick Douglas says in his autobiography: "A keen observer might have detected in our repeated singing of 'O Canaan, sweet Canaan, I am bound for the land of Canaan' something more than a hope of reaching heaven. We meant to reach the North, and the North was our Canaan . . . On our lips it simply meant a speedy pilgrimage to a free state, and deliverance from all the evils of slavery."

Booker T. Washington expresses the same thought of the symbolism latent in the spirituals when he says in "Up From Slavery":

"Most of the verses of the plantation songs had some reference to freedom. True, they had sung those same verses before, but they had been careful to explain that the 'freedom' in these songs referred to the next world, and had no connection with life in this world. Now they gradually threw off the mask and were not afraid to let it be known that the 'freedom' in their songs meant freedom of the body in this world."

Another type of song which sprang from the servitude of the Negro was the work song, and many of these chants were of extraordinary beauty. A contemporary historian, William Francis Allen, said in "Slave Songs of the United States": "I have stood for more than an hour often, listening to them, as they hoisted and lowered the hogsheads and boxes of their cargoes; one man taking the burden of the song (and the slack of the rope) and the others striking in with the chorus. They would sing in this way more than a dozen different songs."

Even such phenomena as the Underground Railway and the Abolitionist Movement which preceded the Civil War were the subjects of many songs. The Underground Railway involved such anxiety and terror that it lent itself easily to dramatic musical interpretation. The song, "Link O' Day," is an eloquent document of that institution which was manned mostly by Quakers, religious enthusiasts, and other abolitionist idealists. Anti-slavery singing circles were formed to spread the gospel, and special songs written for them, generally to the tunes of old hymns. William Lloyd Garrison himself wrote many of these songs, and they were printed in the many pamphlets and "songsters" which appeared between 1840 and the Civil War.

But, just as any liberating movement inspires an avalanche of militant songs, the actual start of the Civil War roused the imagination of American song writers. Every important event, every victory and defeat, produced its quota of songs: marching songs, rallying songs, songs of sentiment, weariness, and, finally, of immense jubilation when the conflict was over. They were sung by millions: in the camp, on the march, going into battle, at the fireside, and at patriotic meetings back home. Thousands of songs were written, and when the course of popular taste and historical evolution sifted them, a great number remained that may still be counted as moving and stirring music. Besides "The Battle Hymn of the Republic," "Tenting on the Old Camp Ground," "Dixie," and "When Johnny Comes Marching Home Again," there were many others that still live on after seventy-five years, notably: "The Battle Cry of Freedom," and "Tramp, Tramp, Tramp the Boys Are Marching." On the Northern side there was "Babylon Is Fallen," "Marching Through Georgia" and "Kingdom Come." In the South, "Carolina," "The Southern Girl," and "The Bonnie Blue Flag."

It is not too surprising that the Emancipation phase of the jubilant Civil War music did not last very long. The Negroes learned quickly enough that their complete freedom was distinctly temporary and that their exaltation could not be sustained. With the advent of the carpet-baggers, the growth of the Ku Klux Klan, and the immediate organization of coercive agencies in the South, which attempted to emasculate emancipation and deprive the Negro of his rights, the black man soon realised that it would not be wise to express his sentiments openly. The jubilant songs which had come with emancipation: "Slavery Chain," "Oh Freedom," and "No More Auction Block," could be sung no more.

Emancipation did bring about one change in the status of the spirituals. Before the Civil War these songs were known and loved in the South. Now they obtained a new popularity in the North, as well, and the spirituals began their long march toward general acceptance. There are definite landmarks in that march —the publication of "Slave Songs of the United States," by Allen, Garrison and Ware, in 1867; the international tour of the Fisk Jubilee Singers in the 1870's; the use of Negro themes by Dvorák in the "New World Symphony" in the '90's; the concert arrangements and adaptations by Henry Burleigh, Nathaniel Dett, and Hall Johnson in the early decades of the present century; the concert careers of Paul Robeson and Roland Hayes; and finally the recognition of the artistry of such singers as Marian Anderson.

Link O'Day

Arrangement
by Elie Siegmeister

LINK O' DAY

AN ELOQUENT SONG which is part of the Abolitionist and Underground Railway record in American History.

"Many of the fugitives," Levi Coffin wrote in his reminiscences in 1877, "came long distances, from Alabama, Mississippi, Louisiana, and, in fact, from all parts of the South. Sometimes the poor hunted creatures had been out so long, living in woods and thickets, that they were almost wild when they came in . . . The pursuit was often very close, and we had to resort to various stratagems in order to elude the pursuers. Sometimes a company of fugitives were scattered and secreted in the neighborhood . . . at other times their route was changed and they were hurried forward with all speed. It was a continual excitement and anxiety . . ."

The song is presented in choral form for which seems best suited. "Link O Day" means daybreak. "Kentry" is "country."

2

Get yeh far away, O!
An' leave yo' massa far behin',
'Fo de link o' day,
'Fo de link o' day.

CHORUS: Run yeh, etc.

3

Dere will come a time, O!
When we will all be free,
We will all be free.

CHORUS: Run yeh, etc.

Heave Away

Arrangement
by Elie Siegmeister

Abolitionist Hymn

Tune: "Old Hundred"

Arrangement by Elie Siegmeister

We ask not that the slave should lie As lies his mas-ter, at his ease, Be-neath a silk-en can-o-py Or in the shade of bloom-ing trees.

2

We ask not "eye for eye," that all,
Who forge the chain and ply the whip,
Should feel their torture; while the thrall
Should wield the scourge of mastership.

3

We mourn not that the man should toil
'Tis nature's need, 'tis God's decree;
But let the hand that tills the soil
Be, like the wind that fans it, free.

145

Lincoln and Liberty

Words: F. A. Simpson
Tune of: "Old Rosin, the Beau"

Arrangement
by Elie Siegmeister

Hur - rah for the choice of the na - tion! Our chief - tain so brave and so true; We'll go for the great re - for - ma - tion, For Lin - coln and Li - ber - ty, too. We'll go for the son of Ken -

tuck - y, The he - ro of Hoo - sier - dom through; The

pride of the Suck - ers so luck - y, For Lin - coln and Li - ber - ty, too.

2

They'll find what by felling and mauling,
Our rail-maker statesman can do;
For the people are ev'rywhere calling,
For Lincoln and Liberty too.
Then up with the banner so glorious,
The star-spangled, red white and blue,
We'll fight till our banner's victorious,
For Lincoln and Liberty, too.

3

Our David's good sling is unerring,
The Slavocrat's giant he slew,
Then shout for the freedom preferring,
For Lincoln and Liberty, too.
We'll go for the son of Kentucky,
The hero of Hoosierdom through;
The pride of the Suckers so lucky,
For Lincoln and Liberty, too.

LINCOLN AND LIBERTY

This was Lincoln's campaign song.

"A man who had been on the roof and was engaged in communicating the results of the ballotings to the mighty mass of outsiders now demanded, by gesture at the skylight over the stage, to know what had happened. One of the secretaries, with a tally sheet in his hands, shouted: 'Fire the salute! Abe Lincoln is nominated!' "

"The City was wild with delight. 'Old Abe' men formed processions and bore rails through the streets. Torrents of liquor were poured down the throats of the multitude. A hundred guns were fired from the top of Tremont House." *Murat Halstead: "Caucuses of 1860"*

Battle Hymn of the Republic

Words by Julia Ward Howe

Arrangement by Elie Siegmeister

Mine eyes have seen the glor - y of the com - ing of the Lord; He is tramp - ling out the vin - tage where the grapes of wrath are stored; He has loosed the fate - ful light - ning of His

2

I have seen Him in the watch-fires of a hundred circling camps;
They have builded Him an altar in the evening dews and damps:
I can read His righteous sentence by the dim and flaring lamps,
His day is marching on.

CHORUS: Glory, glory! Hallelujah, etc.

JOHN BROWN'S BODY

2

He's gone to be a soldier in the army of the Lord,
He's gone to be a soldier in the army of the Lord,
He's gone to be a soldier in the army of the Lord,
His soul is marching on!
CHORUS: Glory, glory, etc.

3

He captured Harper's Ferry with his nineteen men so true,
And he frightened old Virginia till she trembled through and through;
They hung him for a traitor, themselves the traitor crew,
But his soul is marching on!
CHORUS: Glory, glory, etc.

4

John Brown died that the slave might be free,
John Brown died that the slave might be free,
John Brown died that the slave might be free,
But his soul goes marching on!
CHORUS: Glory, glory, etc.

5

The stars of heaven are looking kindly down,
The stars of heaven are looking kindly down,
The stars of heaven are looking kindly down,
On the grave of old John Brown!
CHORUS: Glory, glory, etc.

DIXIE

NOT ALL SOCIAL SONGS and war songs are created in the throes of large emotion and out of patriotic impulse. The South's stirring song, "Dixie," is an example. The author, Dan Emmett, as well known a popular song writer in his day as Cole Porter or George Gershwin in ours, was asked by the manager of Bryant's Minstrels, for whom he worked, to write a new song to be used as a "walk-around" for the next stage show. He sat down that rainy Sunday in 1859, and "Dixie" was ready in time for the show.

It was an immediate success and soon all the minstrel troupes in the country were singing and dancing to it. When the war started, Southern troups appropriated it, in spite of the North's efforts to recapture "Dixie" by writing new lyrics, and it became the marching song of the Confederate army. No one was more dismayed than the composer, a man of Union sympathies, when he became idolized by the South and denounced as a traitor by the North.

Emmett lived to the age of eighty-nine. In spite of the fact that "Dixie," "Old Dan Tucker" and other of his songs are still sung by millions, their composer died conventionally—in complete poverty.

2

Sugar in de gourd and stonny batter,
You'll grow fat and eber fatter,
 Look away, etc:
Den hoe it down and scratch your grabble,
To Dixie's land I'm bound to trabble,
 Look away, etc:

CHORUS: Den I wish, etc.

Dixie

Words and Music
by D. D. Emmet

Arrangement
by Elie Siegmeister

frosty mornin', Look a-way! Look a-way! Look a-way! Dixie Land.

Then I wish I was in Dixie, Hoo-ray! Hoo-ray! In

Dix-ie Land, I'll take my stand To live and die in Dixie; A-way, a-

way, a-way down south in Dixie, A-way, a-way, a-way down south in Dixie.

Tenting To-night

*Words and Music
by Walter Kittredge*

*Arrangement
by Elie Siegmeister*

We're tent-ing to-night on the old camp ground, Give us a song to

cheer Our wear-y hearts, a song of home And friends we love so dear.

Man-y are the hearts that are wear-y to-night, Wish-ing for the war to

cease; Ma - ny are the hearts that are look- ing for the right, To

see the dawn of peace. Tent - ing to-night,

tent - ing to-night, Tent - ing on the old camp ground.

TENTING TONIGHT

WALTER KITTREDGE'S song was sung by both sides in the Civil War. John Tasker Howard believes that this ballad singer of New Hampshire displayed a typical New England business sense when he wrote a song that would appeal to Blue and Gray alike. The sheet music sale ran into the thousands. But a careful reading of the lyrics reveals the fact that the song must have come from his heart. What is more, Kittredge wrote it in 1862, just after he was called to the colors. Its simple melody has caused it to survive as a perennial favorite.

2

We've been tenting to-night on the old camp ground,
Thinking of days gone by,
Of the loved ones at home that gave us the hand,
And the tear that said, "Good-bye."
CHORUS: Many are the hearts, etc.

3

We are tired of war on the old camp ground,
Many are dead and gone,
Of the brave and true who've left their home,
Others been wounded long.
CHORUS: Many are the hearts, etc.

4

We've been fighting to-night on the old camp ground,
Many are lying near;
Some are dead, and some are dying,
Many are in tears.
CHORUS: Many are the hearts, etc.

When Johnny Comes Marching Home

*Words and Music
by Patrick S. Gilmore*

Arrangement
by Elie Siegmeister

158

WHEN JOHNNY COMES MARCHING HOME AGAIN

THERE WERE showmen of the stature of Grover Whalen and Billy Rose long before the 1940 New York World's Fair. In 1869 and 1872, one Patrick S. Gilmore, who was bandmaster of the Union Army, organized such monster Peace Jubilees. They boasted an orchestra of more than 1,000 and a chorus of 10,000 voices, with cannon-fire to emphasize the rhythm of the music, and 100 real, in-the-flesh firemen to pound the anvils for the *Anvil Chorus* from Trovatore.

Mr. Gilmore claimed the authorship of the song, "When Johnny Comes Marching Home Again." He is reported to have told a friend that he took down the melody when he heard a Negro singing the song. Even the most untutored audience, however, would suspect, upon hearing the song, that the Negro's name may have been Pat Reilly. That suspicion deepens when we learn that Gilmore himself was a native of Ireland.

"Johnny" remains a rousing tune. Like other good songs, it has inspired many parodies, one of which, "Billy McGee, McGaw," has words descended from an old Scotch song, "Twa Corbies."

2

The old church bell will peal with joy,
Hurrah! Hurrah!
To welcome home our darling boy,
Hurrah! Hurrah!
The village lads and lassies say
With roses they will strew the way,
And we'll all feel gay
When Johnny comes marching home.

3

Get ready for the Jubilee,
Hurrah! Hurrah!
We'll give the hero three times three,
Hurrah! Hurrah!
The laurel wreath is ready now
To place upon his loyal brow
And we'll all feel gay
When Johnny comes marching home.

4

In eighteen hundred and sixty-one,
Hurrah! Hurrah!
That was when the war begun,
Hurrah! Hurrah!
In eighteen hundred and sixty-two,
Both sides were falling to
And we'll all drink stone wine,
When Johnny comes marching home.

5

In eighteen hundred and sixty-three,
Hurrah! Hurrah!
Abe Lincoln set the darkies free,
Hurrah! Hurrah!
In eighteen hundred and sixty-three
Old Abe set the darkies free,
And we'll all drink stone wine,
When Johnny comes marching home.

6

In eighteen hundred and sixty-four,
Hurrah! Hurrah!
Abe called for five hundred thousand more,
Hurrah! Hurrah!
In eighteen hundred and sixty-five,
They talked rebellion—strife;
And we'll all drink stone wine
When Johnny comes marching home.

2

Said one old crow unto his mate,
Billy Magee Magaw!
Said one old crow unto his mate,
Billy Magee Magaw!
Said one old crow unto his mate
"What shall we do for grub to ate?"

CHORUS: And they all, *etc.*

3

"There lies a horse on yonder plain."
Billy Magee Magaw!
"There lies a horse on yonder plain."
Billy Magee Magaw!
"There lies a horse on yonder plain,
'Twas by some cruel butcher slain."

CHORUS: And they all, *etc.*

4

"We'll perch ourselves on his backbone."
Billy Magee Magaw!
"We'll perch ourselves on his backbone."
Billy Magee Magaw!
"We'll perch ourselves on his backbone,
And pick his eyes out one by one."

CHORUS: And they all, *etc.*

All Quiet on the Potomac

Words by Lamarr Fontaine
Music by J. H. Hewitt

Arrangement
by Elie Siegmeister

"All qui - et a - long the Po - to - mac to - night," Ex -

cept here and there a stray Pick - et Is shot as he walks on his

beat to and fro By a rif - le-man hid in the thick - et 'Tis

noth-ing, a pri-vate or two now and then Will not count in the news of the bat-tle: Not an of-fi-cer lost, on-ly one of the men Moan-ing out all a-lone the death rat-tle. "All qui-et a-long the Po-to-mac to-night."

ALL QUIET ON THE POTOMAC

IN THE FIRST YEARS of the Civil War the words "All quiet on the Potomac" were just as familiar to every newspaper reader as the phrase "All quiet on the Western Front" became to modern readers. It referred to the continued stalemate on the eastern front. The composer turned the catch-phrase into a song. Some of the lines ("Ha! Mary, goodbye!") are scarcely thrilling today, but they must have struck a distinctly human note in an age that loved musical titles like "The Last Hope," "The Vacant Chair," "Rock Me to Sleep, Mother," and "Grandfather's Clock."

2

"All quiet along the Potomac to-night,"
There the soldiers lie peacefully dreaming
And their tents in the rays of the clear autumn moon
And the rays of the camp-fires are gleaming.

A tremulous sigh as the gentle night wind
Through the forest leaves slowly is creeping,
While the stars up above, with their glittering eyes
Keep guard o'er the army while sleeping.

"All quiet along the Potomac to-night."

3

Hark! Was it the night wind that rustles the leaves?
Was it the moonlight so wondrously flashing?
It looked like a rifle! "Ha! Mary, good-bye!"
And his life-blood is ebbing and plashing.

"All quiet along the Potomac to-night."
No sound save the sound of the river;
While soft falls the dew on the face of the dead,
The "picket's" off duty forever.

"All quiet along the Potomac to-night."

Weeping Sad and Lonely

Words by C. C. Sawyer
Music by Henry Tucker

Arrangement
by Elie Siegmeister

Dear - est love, do you re - mem - ber, When we last did meet, How you told me that you loved me, Kneel - ing at my feet? Oh! How proud you stood be-

fore me, In your suit of blue,_____

mf
When you vowed to me and coun - try, Ev - er to be true.

Weep - ing, sad and lone - ly, Hopes and fears how vain!

When this cru - el war is ov - er, Pray - ing that we meet a - gain!

8va___

165

Year of Jubilo

by Henry C. Work

*Arrangement
by Elie Siegmeister*

Say, dark-ies, hab you seen de mas-sa, Wid de muff-stash on his face, Go long de road some time dis morn-in', Like he goin' to leave de place? He seen a smoke way up de rib-ber, Where de Lin-kun gun-boats lay; He took his hat, and lef' ber-ry sud-den, An' I 'spec he's run a-

Chorus

way. De mas - sa run, ha! ha! De dark - ey stay, ho! ho! It

mus' be now de King-dom com-in' An' de year ob Ju - bi - lo!

2

He' six foot one way, two foot t'udder
An' he weigh t'ree hundred pound,
His coat's so big he couldn't pay de tailor
An' it won' go half way round.
He drill so much dey calls him cap'n,
An' he gets so mighty tanned,
I 'spec he'll try to fool dem Yankees
For to tink he's contraband.

3

De darkeys got so lonesome libin'
In de log hut on de lawn,
Dey move dere t'ings into massa's parlor,
For to keep it while he's gone.
Dar's wine an' cider in de kitchen
An' de darkeys dey'll hab some;
I 'spose dey'll all be confiscated,
When de Linkun soldiers come.

IT IS HARD to think of the man who looked like both of the Smith Brothers as a writer of smash-hit tunes of his day. Yet Henry Clay Work, bearded and patriarchal, was seldom absent from the best-seller list in music. He was the author and composer of "Grandfather's Clock," "The Ship that Never Returned," and many another tune that has been pumped out of many a wheezy parlor organ. His song, "Come Home. Father," was a boon and a standby for temperance leagues for years. But he was perhaps best known as the composer of patriotic and anti-slavery songs. His father had been in jail for operating a station of the Underground Railroad in Illinois.

"Marching Through Georgia," and "Babylon is Fallen" are rousing tunes, but "Kingdom Come" was Work's most successful song. After Lee's surrender the Northern army sang it as they marched into Richmond.

Go Down Moses

Arrangement
by Elie Siegmeister

Go down Moses, "Way down in E-gypt's land;

Tell ole Pha raoh— Let my peo-ple go.

When Is-rael was in E-gypt's land, Let my peo-ple go; Op-

pressed so hard they could not stand, Let my peo-ple go.

GO DOWN, MOSES

LAWRENCE GELLERT tells of coming upon two colored boys who were sitting on a third one in the middle of a road in Georgia and systematically removing his various articles of clothing. When Gellert bent down to help the victim jumped up:

"Tha's awright, boss. We's jes' playin' ' sp'ilin' de' Gypshuns.' "

"Despoiling the Egyptians," now a children's game, was, in slavery times, a very real wish on the part of those whose favorite Biblical heroes were Joshua, David, Moses, men who could stand up and say, "Let my people go."

"Go Down, Moses" is more than a song. It is the cry of a people.

2

Thus saith the Lord, bold Moses said;
    Let my people go;
If not I'll smite your first born dead,
    Let my people go.
CHORUS: Go down Moses, etc.

3

No more shall they in bondage toil,
    Let my people go;
Let them come out with Egypt's spoil,
    Let my people go.
CHORUS: Go down Moses, etc.

4

The Lord told Moses what to do,
    Let my people go;
To lead the children of Israel thro',
    Let my people go.
CHORUS: Go down Moses, etc.

5

When they had reached the other shore,
    Let my people go;
They sang a song of triumph o'er
    Let my people go.
CHORUS: Go down Moses, etc.

Deep River

*Arrangement
by Elie Siegmeister*

gos - pel feast. that pro - mised land, That land— where all is

peace? Walk - in to heav - en and

take my seat And cast my crown at Je - sus' feet. Lord.

Never Said a Mumbalin' Word

*Arrangement
by Elie Siegmeister*

Oh, dey whupped him up de hill, up de hill, up de hill, Oh, dey

whupped him up de hill an' he ne - ver said a mum-ba-lin' word, Oh, dey

whupped him up de hill an' he ne - ver said a'mum-ba-lin' word, He jes'

hung down his head, an' he cried.

NEVER SAID A MUMBLIN' WORD

IN AN ADDRESS delivered July 9, 1862, Mr. J. N. McKim said:

"I asked one of these blacks where they got these songs. 'Dey make 'em, sah!'

" 'How do they make them?'

" 'I'll tell you, it's dis way. My master call me up, and order me a short peck of corn and a hundred lash. My friends see it, and is sorry for me. When dey come to de praise-meeting dat night dey sing about it. Some's very good singers and know how; and dey work it in—work it in, you know, till they get it right; and dat's de way!' "

2

Oh, dey crowned him wid a thorny crown, thorny crown, thorny crown,
Oh, dey crowned him wid a thorny crown, an' he never said a mumbalin'
    word,
Oh, dey crowned him wid a thorny crown, an' he never said a mumbalin'
    word,
He jes' hung down his head, an' he cried.

3

Well, dey nailed him to de cross, to de cross, to de cross,
Well, dey nailed him to de cross, an' he never said a mumbalin' word,
Well, dey nailed him to de cross, an' he never said a mumbalin' word,
He jes' hung down his head an' he cried.

4

Well, dey pierced him in de side, in de side, in de side,
Well, dey pierced him in de side, an' he never said a mumbalin' word,
Well, dey pierced him in de side, an' he never said a mumbalin' word,
Den he hung down his head, an' he died.

Little David

Arrangement
by Elie Siegmeister

He killed Go - li - ath and shou - ted for joy. Lit - tle Da - vid,

Little David, play on yo' harp, Hallelu! Hallelu!
Little David, play on yo' harp, Hallelu!
Little David, play on yo' harp, Hallelu! Hallelu!
Little David, play on yo' harp, Hallelu!

2

Joshua was the son of Nun
He never would quit till the work was done.

CHORUS: Little David, etc.

3

Done told you once, done told you twice,
There's sinners in Hell for shootin' dice.

CHORUS: Little David, etc.

LITTLE DAVID

THIS IS ONE of the most familiar of spirituals, and an excellent example of the singing method that was common among large congregations.

James Weldon Johnson has pointed out in his autobiography that it was necessary to have someone with a strong voice who knew just the appropriate tune to sing and the appropriate time to sing it. The leader had to pitch it in the right key and he had to have all the leading lines memorized "because the congregation sings only the refrains and re- plies. Every ear in the church is fixed upon him, and if he becomes mixed in his lines or forgets them, the responsibility is directly on his shoulders."

This Is A Sin-trying World

*Arrangement
by Elie Siegmeister*

don't know whe-ther I'll ev-er get to Heav'n or no.

CHORUS:

O, this is a sin-tryin' world—(High Heavens!)
This is a sin-tryin' world—(Hard trials!)
This is a sin-tryin' world—(Crown of Life!)
This is a sin-tryin' world.

2

Jordan's stream is chilly and wide;
None can cross but the sanctified.

CHORUS:

O, this is a sin-tryin' world—(Cold Jordan!)
This is a sin-tryin' world—(Deep and wide!)
This is a sin-trying' world—(Can't you cross it!)
This is a sin-tryin' world.

THIS IS A SIN-TRYIN' WORLD

IT IS VIRTUALLY IMPOSSIBLE to catch the spirit of true folk song on the printed page. "This Is a Sin-Tryin' World" represents one of those improvised revival-meeting spirituals that teem with excitement and tension. The cumulative emotion that goes into the half-sung, half-shouted interjections of "Oh, Jesus!," "Hard Trials!," the ecstatic voice of the leader and the crushing unison of the entire congregation in the chorus can only be interpreted and understood by those who have heard Negro revival meetings.

Blind Man

*Arrangement
by Elie Siegmeister*

Blin' man stood on de way an' cried, Blin' man
stood on de way an' cried, Cry - in', "O Lawd,
show me de way!" Blin' man stood on de way an' cried.

2
Cryin', "Help me, O Lawd, if you please!"
Cryin', "Help me, O Lawd, if you please!"
Cryin', "O Lawd, show me de way!"
Blin' man stood on de way an' cried.

3
When I was a sinner I stood on de way an' cried,
When I was a sinner I stood on de way an' cried,
Cryin', "O Lawd, show me de way!"
Blin' man stood on de way an' cried.

BLIND MAN

TRUE ART speaks to all men above barriers of place and language. This
song seems to speak for all those who have cried out, "Show me the
way!"

7. Courting, Love and Children

It used to be pointed out by the fashionable critics of American culture that the Yankee was incapable of creating what every other race had produced—a body of native folk song. Various explanations for this were offered, usually by visiting lecturers at ladies' afternoon teas: that the American was by nature cold-blooded and unmusical; that he was too preoccupied with commercial and material success; that folk song was the product of a peasant class and could not be produced by an "individualistic" nation; that we lacked tradition, roots in the soil; and, finally, that we were too young, too hybrid, too immature as a people to have the "creative gift."

That was the first stage. After several dozens of volumes of native songs had been published, the visiting authorities finally were constrained to admit that yes, there was some local music in this country, but it could all be shown to be of foreign origin. Even that astute and catholic observer, Cecil Sharp, who did much to bring attention to and record the music of the Appalachian region, could not bring himself to see in it anything other than a residue of what the early settlers had brought over with them. Although he was the first to discover and publish songs such as "Ground Hog," "Kentucky Moonshiner," "John Hardy" and "Come all you Arkansas Girls" which are as American as corn pone, chewing tobacco or Boston baked beans, he assumed that they must naturally be the reflection of something that happened in England some centuries ago, and he published them all under the title, "English Folk Songs in the Southern Appalachians." Sharp, of course, found many descendants of the old English and Scotch ballads and folk songs still alive in the mountains; in fact he was the first to notice and point out that they were even more alive here than in his native England. But to him everything he heard here was English.

About 1930, as a result of Sharp's researches, and those of Lunsford, Lomax, Richardson, and many others, it began to be generally conceded that there was a certain amount of native production; but still, it was considered something peculiar to very restricted areas and to a very special type of American. In the general mind these were: (1) the hill-billy mountaineer, who was always supposed to be feudin', moonshinin' or sittin' around strummin' a banjo; (2) the cowboy who, of course, was always whoopee-ti-yoing it over the lone prairree; and, of course, (3) the southern Negro who was pictured as intoning spirituals all day long, while he picked cotton, interrupting occasionally only to shout, "Praise de Lawd!" or "Hallelujah!" While this picture may seem overdrawn, it is the one we still get from Hollywood and from short stories in the weekly magazines.

It is only recently that this fiction of an uncreative, or of a musically limited America has collapsed. With the spread of interest and research it had been discovered that there is practically no part of this land without its treasure of folk and traditional song. Not only the mountains but the foot-hills, the flatlands, the tide-water regions, New England, the midwest, the far west; even the cities have yielded a rich harvest for those who know how to hear. Vermont, hitherto considered a dour and unmusical state, has yielded over 200 native tunes, many dealing with local events. Florida, of which nothing was known in the way of music, has recently turned in over a thousand songs! Ohio, Nebraska, Michigan, Oklahoma—spoken of only a few years ago by some of our snobbish high priests of intelligence as "the great intellectual desert," the "hinterland," the home of the "booboisie"—all these have yielded ballads old and new, songs, fiddle tunes, play party and square dances, prison wails, work songs, folk hymns, shanties and blues. The Library of Congress alone has, according to the latest report, more than 15,000 phonograph discs of native song, which have scarcely begun to be studied, much less notated and made available. From Texas, John and Alan Lomax report one family alone which had five hundred tunes in their repertory.

Far from being confined to any special place, or being the property of any particular set of Americans, our traditional music is hidden everywhere. Some of it gets around in the strangest ways. Mary Eddy tells of recording one of the most attractive versions of the "Gypsy Laddie" ballad from the singing of a Russian Jew who had learned it in Utah while living among the Mormons. From Scotland to Salt Lake to the banks of the Wabash via the singing of someone who probably came from Minsk or Odessa!

One of the present authors, working in his study, was interrupted by the cry of a peddler outside his window. He notated the peddler's call, and when it was performed at a Town Hall concert a few months later, the reviewers singled it out as a characteristic bit of American folk-lore! Three songs were picked up during intermissions between rehearsals in the Columbia Broadcasting System studios in New York—where one might ordinarily expect the utmost sophistication—from professional singers who remembered them from father's or grandmother's singing back home in Indiana, Maine and Oklahoma.

Folk music, then, is a broad and general expression of our country. Folk songs tell of humble incidents of everyday life, treat universal themes in an American manner. They deal with courtship, love and marriage; the old maid and the scolding wife; the rocking cradle. There are animal songs and children's game songs, many of them evolved from the songs of adults.

Some of our folk songs are derived from ancient ballads. Others have the tang of the Green Mountains, the Appalachians, the Ozarks. Their language and their musical line stem out of rural life. They tell us what happens in Podunk, Squash Hollow, Strawberry Point. In them we have portraits of brisk young lovers, hen-pecked husbands, lonely girls, children at play, saucy old maids, housewives who have to work from morning till night. They lead us through an Arkansas kitchen, an Ohio front room, a Vermont bedroom, and a Mississippi backyard.

In telling the story of America, these songs bring to life once more the traditional lore of world culture. Since Homer's day children have been singing of what the Blackbird told the Crow, of how the Frog and the Mouse got on together. Only here the blackbird has a Yankee twang and the frog courts the mouse with a Southern or Western drawl. Old Druidic rituals appear once more in the game song of the "Old Woman All Skin and Bones." Ancient mystic incantations may lie hidden in the nonsense refrains, "Scratch-a-fol-lee-fol-lol-i-dee-i-day," or "Ram yam gilliam, dandoo, ah," —although to the modern singer they are merely manifestations of a simple *joie de vivre*, like Shakespeare's "Hey Nonny Nonny," the cowboy's "Yippee-i-yay" or Tin Pan Alley's "Hi-de-ho."

But whether ancient or modern, the common song-lore of America cannot be crushed. Differing from the more sophisticated art, which can be sung only by trained interpreters and which it is easy to kill by bad performance, the traditional songs can't be killed by screechy, rattly or wheezy voices, or by "wrong interpretations."

Although temporarily submerged by the fabricated tunes of Tin Pan Alley, radio and Hollywood, these tunes can "take it." Unlike the fragile products of the Broadway musical assembly line whose life span has dwindled to a matter of weeks, genuine folk songs, like the old Model-T Ford, were built to last, to take all the bumps and knocks and come up sturdy and strong when all of today's radio hits have turned to dust.

The Chickens Are A-crowing

*Arrangement
by Elie Siegmeister*

The chick - ens they are crow - ing, a- crow - ing, a- crow-ing, The
chick - ens they are crow - ing, for it is al - most day - light.

2

My mother she will scold me, will scold me, will scold me,
My mother she will scold me for staying away all night.

3

My father he'll uphold me, uphold me, uphold me,
My father he'll uphold me and say I'd done just right.

4

I won't go home till morning, till morning, till morning,
I won't go home till morning, and I'll stay with the girls all night.

5

The chickens they are crowing, a-crowing, a-crowing,
The chickens they are crowing, for it is almost daylight.

When Boys Go Courting

*Arrangement
by Elie Siegmeister*

When boys go a-court - ing they dress up so fine, To cheat the poor girls is all their de-sign. They'll sit there and tat - ter and tat - ter and lie, They'll keep up the girls 'til they're read - y to die. La - rey - wo, wo, _____ wo, la - rey - wo.

WHEN BOYS GO A-COURTING

A LILTING TUNE proving that this is a man's world. One of the theories of the origin of nonsense syllables refrains is that they were sung in polite company to replace lines of Rabelaisian character. One wonders what the original words of the phrase, "Larey-wo, wo, larey-wo," must have been.

The song is sometimes used for dancing.

2

The girls they be wearied, they'll rise up and say:
"Boys, I'm sleepy, I wish you'd go away.
You're nothing but false-hearted and such I do scorn."
Before you go home you will lie in the barn.

CHORUS: Larey-wo, *etc.*

3

Next morning, next morning, the boys they'll rise,
Brush off the straws and wipe open their eyes,
They'll mount on their horses and home they will ride,
Like false-hearted fellows all puffed up with pride.

CHORUS: Larey-wo, *etc.*

4

When they get there they'll stagger and reel,
Sing: "Bless all the girls, how sleepy I feel,
No wife to control me, no children to brawl,"
How happy this young man keeps bachelor hall.

CHORUS: Larey-wo, *etc.*

I Must and I Will Get Married

*Arrangement
by Elie Siegmeister*

One morn - ing, one morn - ing, the weath-er be - ing fine, The

moth-er and the daugh-ter walked out to take the air; And as they were a-

-walk-ing this maid be-gan to vow: "I must and I will get

mar-ried, I'm in the no-tion now." now."

1st and others   *last*

I MUST AND WILL BE MARRIED

A DECLARATION of feminine perseverence, calling to mind George Bernard Shaw's cryptic observation, a man chases a woman until she catches him. "If you want to go a-courting" goes with a swing and a lollop, the more diverting because of the old-fashioned character of the tune.

2

"Oh daughter, oh daughter, 'tis hold your foolish tongue,
What makes you want to marry? You know you are too young."
"I'm sixteen now, dear mother, and that you must allow,
I must and I will get married, I'm in the notion now."

3

"Suppose you were to try, dear, and could not find a man?"
"Oh, never mind, dear mother, for there are Miller Sam.
He calls me milk and honey, go milking of my cow,
I must and I will get married, I'm in the notion now."

4

"Suppose he were to fool with you as he has done before?"
"Oh, never mind, dear mother, for there are plenty more.
For there is Jack the farmer, goes whistling to his plough.
I must and I will get married, I'm in the notion now."

If You Want to Go A-courting

Arrangement
by Elie Siegmeister

If you want to go a-court ing, I'll tell you where to go,

Just down yon-der, just down be-low. The old man, old wo-man

gone from the home, And the girls all mad with their

heads not combed, And the girls all mad with their heads not combed.

IF YOU WANT TO GO A-COURTING

An episode of backwoods wooing, with a warning note on the obstacles, both culinary and military, to be overcome. The perky tune is tough as the meat that wouldn't carve, as determined as the pappy with his double-barreled gun.

2

They haven't got sense to bake a pound of bread,
They'll throw on a log heap as high as my head,
They'll rake out the ashes and then they'll throw
A little of what's called dough, boys, dough,
A little of what's called dough, boys, dough.

3

When the supper comes on and they ask me to eat,
When they call on me to carve up the meat;
One old knife and one old fork,
I sawed about an hour and could not make a mark,
I sawed about an hour and could not make a mark.

4

One of the girls said, "Wait, Mister, wait."
Then just kept sawing till I got it on the plate,
Then just kept sawing till I got it on the floor,
Then up with my foot and kicked it out of door,
Then up with my foot and kicked it out of door.

5

The girls cried, "Mister, you'd better run,
Yonder comes my daddy with a double barreled gun!"
I'll stand my ground as brave as a bear,
I'll tangle my fingers with the old man's hair,
I'll tangle my fingers with the old man's hair.

He's Gone Away

Arrangement
by Elie Siegmeister

Slowly Sustained

I'm goin' a - way for to stay a lit - tle while, But I'm com - ing back, if I go ten thou - sand miles; Oh, who will tie your shoes? And who will glove your hand? And who will kiss those ru - by lips when I am

gone? Look a - way, look a - way ov - er Yan - dro.

Hold back

pp

2

He's gone away for to stay a little while,
But he's comin' back if he goes ten thousand miles.
Oh, it's pappy'll tie my shoes,
And mammy'll glove my hands,
And you will kiss my ruby lips when you come back!
Look away, look away over Yandro.

HE'S GONE AWAY

THIS IS one of the most haunting melodies that have come from the mountain district. There is complete freedom of melody and an effect of inspired improvisation springing from poignant emotion. The rhythm is so free and the melody so perfectly mated to the verse that the bar lines which editors have used appear here as clumsy and superfluous.

This song is a remarkable example of the changes wrought upon an old English original, which in itself has many versions, through the influences of the mountain folk and the Negro people.

I'm Sad and I'm Lonely

*Arrangement
by Elie Siegmeister*

190

The Lonesome Grove

Arrangement
by Elie Siegmeister

Foggy Dew

*Arrangement
by Elie Siegmeister*

One night she came to my bedside,
So bitterly she did weep.
Come to my bed, my pretty fair Miss,
Get out of the foggy dew.

Towards the first part of the year,
She took pale in the face;
Along towards the latter part of the year,
She got bigger round the waist.

Along towards the last of the year,
She brought me a son.
Now you see as well as I,
What the foggy dew has done.

I taken this girl and married her,
I loved her as my life,
And I taken this girl and married her,
She made me a virtuous wife.

I never throwed it up to her,
Damn my eyes if I had;
For every time the baby cried,
I'd think of the foggy dew.

The Devil and the Farmer's Wife

Arrangement
by Elie Siegmeister

193

carry a-way," Scratch-a-fol-lee- fol- lol-fol-li-dee-i-

day. day.

2

"And now," says the farmer, "It's I am undone."
Fol-lol-fol-li-dee-i-lee.
"And now," says the farmer, "It's I am undone,
For the devil has come for my oldest son."
Scratch-a-fol-lee-fol-lol-fol-li-dee-i-day.

3

"Oh no," says the devil, "it's not your oldest son."
Fol-lol-fol-li-dee-i-lee.
"Oh no," says the devil, "it's not your oldest son,"
But that old scolding woman's the very one."
Scratch-a-fol-lee-fol-lol-fol-li-dee-i-day.

4

The devil he got her right onto his back,
Fol-lol-fol-li-dee-i-lee.
The devil he got her right onto his back,
And down into Hell he went snappety crack.
Scratch-a-fol-lee-fol-lol-fol-li-dee-i-day.

He set the young devils preparing some chains,
Fol-lol-fol-li-dee-i-lee.
He set the young devils preparing some chains,
She up with her foot and kicked out all their brains.
Scratch-a-fol-lee-fol-lol-fol-li-dee-i-day.

6

"Oh now," says the devil, "we'll h'st her up higher."
Fol-lol-fol-li-dee-i-lee.
"Oh now," says the devil, "we'll h'st her up higher."
She up with her foot and kicked nine in the fire.
Scratch-a-fol-lee-fol-lol-fol-li-dee-i-day.

7

The devil he got her right onto his back,
Fol-lol-fol-li-dee-i-lee.
The devil he got her right onto his back,
And back to the farmer went snappety-crack.
Scratch-a-fol-lee-fol-lol-fol-li-dee-i-day.

8

Says he, "Old lady, did you fare very well?"
Fol-lol-fol-li-dee-i-lee.
Says he, "Old lady, did you fare very well?"
Says she, "Old man, I flattened all hell."
Scratch-a-fol-lee-fol-lol-fol-li-dee-i-day.

9

Now you see what these old women can do,
Fol-lol-fol-li-dee-i-lee.
Now you see what these old women can do,
They can whip old men and devils too,
Scratch-a-fol-lee-fol-lol-fol-li-dee-i-day.

THE DEVIL AND THE FARMER'S WIFE

A BALLAD from the New England pie belt that is sung fervently—and privately—by the henpecked husbands of the world.

There is some evidence that the Henry Purcell was the composer of this tune's earliest ancestor.

The Single Girl

*Arrangement
by Elie Siegmeister*

When I was single, my shoes they did screak;
Now I am married, my shoes they do leak.

When I was single, I eat biscuit and pie;
Now I am married, it's eat corn-bread or die.

Three little babies, crying for bread,
With none to give them, I wish I was dead.

Wash their little feet and send them to sch[ool]
Along comes a drunkard and calls them a [...]

Dishes to wash, springs to go to,
When you are married, you've all to do.

Oh, I wish I was a single girl again.
Good Lord, I wish I was a single girl again.

Go to Sleepy

*Arrangement
by Elie Siegmeister*

Slow, Tenderly

Go ter sleep, go ter sleep, Go ter sleep - y, mam - my's ba - by, When you wake you shall have cake, Go ter sleep - y, mam-my's ba - by.

2

Go ter sleep, go ter sleep,
Go ter sleepy, mammy's baby,
All de horses in de stable
B'longs ter mammy's little baby.

GO TO SLEEPY

A LOVELY DROWSY TUNE, hummed over many a cradle by both white and negro women of the South. The words are descended from much older lullabies.

Itiskit Itaskit

*Arrangement
by Elie Siegmeister*

ITISKIT, ITASKIT

THIS GAME-SONG, known to children the country over, seems to have an archaic, timeless character. It is currently sung in slightly different versions as a nursery rhyme ("It's raining, it's pouring"); a lullaby ("Bye, baby Bunting, Daddy's gone a-hunting"); a taunting song ("Cry, baby, cry"); as another game song ("Little Sally Sand"); and as a wishing song on rainy days ("Rain, rain, go away; Come again some other day; Little Willie wants to play").

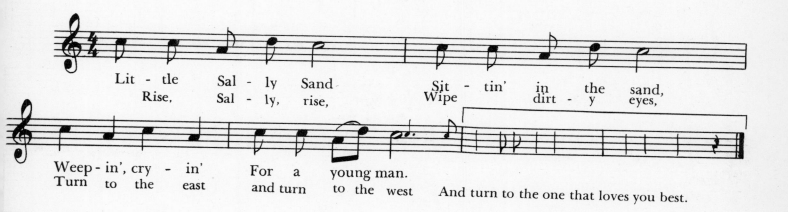

Lit - tle Sal - ly Sand   Sit - tin' in the sand,
Rise, Sal - ly, rise,   Wipe dirt - y eyes,

Weep - in', cry - in'   For a young man.
Turn to the east   and turn to the west   And turn to the one that loves you best.

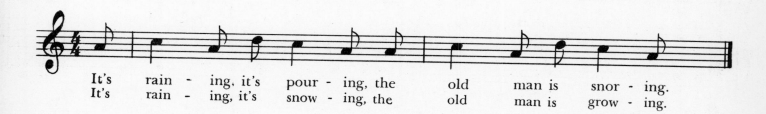

It's rain - ing, it's pour - ing, the old man is snor - ing.
It's rain - ing, it's snow - ing, the old man is grow - ing.

Bye ba - by bunt - ing,   Dad - dy's gone a - hunt - ing   To
catch a lit - tle rab - bit skin   To wrap my ba - by bunt - ing in.

Here Come Three Merchants A-riding

*Arrangement
by Elie Siegmeister*

2

What are you riding here for,
Here for, here for,
What are you riding here for,
Innamen, senaman, see.

3

We're riding here to get married,
Married, married,
We're riding here to get married,
Innamen, senaman, see.

4

You're awful dirty and ragged,
Ragged, ragged,
You're awful dirty and ragged,
Innamen, senaman, see.

5

We're just as good as you are,
You are, you are,
We're just as good as you are,
Innamen, senaman, see.

6

Which one of us will you have, sir,
Have, sir, have, sir,
Which one of us will you have, sir,
Innamen, senaman, see.

7

The fairest one that I can see, sir,
See, sir, see, sir,
The fairest one that I can see, sir,
Innamen, senaman, see.

Old Woman All Skin and Bone

Arrangement
by Elie Siegmeister

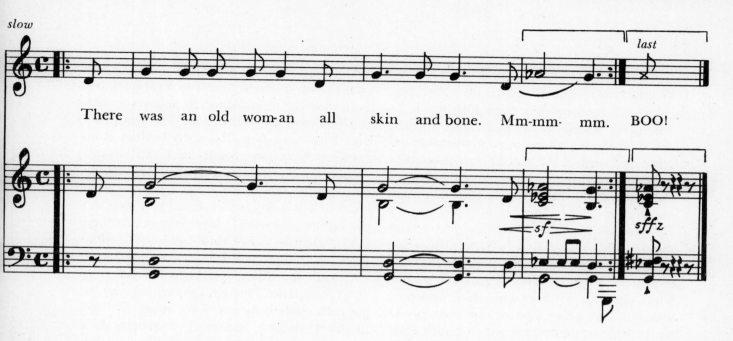

There was an old wom-an all skin and bone. Mm-mm- mm. BOO!

She went to the churchyard all alone. Oo-oo-oo.

She looked up and looked down. Oo-oo-oo.

She saw a corpse lie on the ground. Oo-oo-oo.

"Father, father," so she said. Oo-oo-oo.

"Shall I look so when I am dead?" Oo-oo-oo.

The sexton to her made reply. Oo-oo-oo.

"Yes, my darling, by and by." BOO!

THE VERSE has a gruesomeness in which children appear to delight. Especially do they delight in the screech supposed to come with the sight of the corpse.

To play the game, each object and person in the verses is represented by a player. The one who takes the part of the old woman approaches the corpse, which lies at the feet of the sexton. The players sing as the old woman walks toward the "churchyard," and the moaning chant is broken by the shrill scream of the corpse as it arises abruptly and gives chase to the other players. If the corpse can catch another player, that one becomes the old woman.

8. Cripple Creek to Old Smoky

WHILE THE conventional picture that presented all genuine American folk music as "mountain songs" is one-sided and false, it would be equally wrong to go to the other extreme and neglect the special contribution to our native culture of the people of the Ozarks, and particularly of the Appalachian mountain country.

Almost all sections of the country have characteristic folk music. But the several thousand square miles included in the mountain districts of western Virginia, West Virginia, North and South Carolina, Kentucky and Tennessee have something no other part of our country can equal. It is music tangy as a crab-apple, ebullient as hard cider.

Some years ago it was quite the thing in certain circles to exclaim over these quaint mountaineers who still spoke Elizabethan English and sang ancient ballads of lords and ladies. But in 1917 Cecil Sharp, although he came over to collect just that sort of material, noted that the Appalachian country was not, as some have given the impression, a sort of animated musical waxworks, in which the dead memories of past centuries were miraculously preserved and resuscitated. He found it remarkable that it was not only old people who sang folk songs, as in England, but also children, boys in their teens, people of all ages. It struck him that here was a community in which, for one reason or another, the natural gift for ballad-making and improvisation had not been lost; where musical utterance through song, which in more "civilized" regions is the property of a select and trained elite, was still the common property of all.

Since Sharp visited the Appalachians, things have changed there. Electricity and concrete highways now pass through the remote valleys and folk singers show their wares not only in some lonesome grove but also at annual festivals which bring audiences from miles around and are broadcast on the radio. The lonely settlers have been bought out by lumber companies, or have gone to work in the mill towns.

But through all this, the characteristic mountain speech, dances and songs have not been lost. Girls and boys still kick a lively step and the fiddler and banjo player still get in their licks in square dance tunes such as "Cotton-eyed Joe," "Bucking Mule," "Cackling Hen," "Who Bit the Tater," "Cornstalk Fiddle," or "Old Joe Clarke," though the evening may begin with modern dances to the radio. "Ballits" of local doings: robberies, murders, love tragedies, like "McAfee's Confession," "Darling Cora," "Wild Bill Jones," or "John Hardy," continue finding their way around. And there are plenty of mountain troubadours on the hoof, like Bascom Lunsford, Jim Garland, Sarie Ogan and Aunt Molly Jackson, whose authentic sliding, gliding, high-pitched creaky voices tell of new days in the mountains —of the coming of the good and bad years, of the WPA and TVA, of new heroes and bad men whose names get around over the grapevine telegraph of song to places where newspapers are still not common. Far from killing them off, "civilization" has widened the mountain balladeer's scope, given him new and more exciting subjects to put into song.

Although it has been much caricatured, the "mountain intonation" is still a live and original kind of musical speech. To the unaccustomed ear it is nothing but a shrill, flat, unappealing mannerism. But once you have broken down your concert hall prejudices, the particular vocal, nasal and guttural inflections— which are as difficult to describe in print as they are to set down in notes—have a charm and color that are unique. There is nothing fixed or static about this intonation. A song will be sung a little differently each time it is performed. Notes which seem like sharps at first hearing turn out to be naturals a second time; a third time they are in between; and on a fourth hearing they seem to glide back and forth between sharp and natural. This is as true of the mountain fiddler as of the singer.

The same is true of rhythmic values. A song which is in 3/4 time on Monday turns up in 4/4 on Tuesday. And on Wednesday it has a few measures of 3/4 and the rest in 5/4. To those accustomed to written music which is generally better behaved, all this is very confusing at first. But after a while the fascination of these ever-fluctuating, ever-growing and changing melodic and rhythmic patterns dawns on you, and you are won over. Here is the feeling of what music must once have been like, before it became a business. Here is a people, all of them musicians, who still possess that instinctive knack of putting simple experiences of life into an immediate and direct musical speech without thinking first of regulations, rules, "audience appeal" or market. Here is one of the musical well-springs of America.

Sourwood Mountain

Arrangement
by Elie Siegmeister

Chick- ens a-crow - in' on Sour- wood Mount- ain, Ho-dee- ing-dong- doo - dle- all- a- day. So man - y pret - ty girls I can't count 'em, Ho-dee- ing-dong- doo - dle- all- a- day.

2

I got a gal at the head o' the holler,
Ho-dee-ing-dong-doodle-all-a-day,
She won't come an' I won't foller,
Ho-dee-ing-dong-doodle-all-a-day.

SOURWOOD MOUNTAIN

THIS IS one of the gayest and most popular of all the mountain fiddle tunes. There are as many variants of this song as there are counties and communities in the Kentucky mountains.

3

My true love is a blue-eyed daisy,
Ho-dee-ing-dong-doodle-all-a-day.
If I don't get her I'll go crazy,
Ho-dee-ing-dong-doodle-all-a-day.

4

She sits up with old Si Hall,
Ho-dee-ing-dong-doodle-all-a-day.
Me an' Jeff can't go there at all,
Ho-deeing-dong-doodle-all-a-day.

5

Big dog bark an' the little one bite you,
Ho-dee-ing-dong-doodle-all-a-day.
Big gal court an' the little one marry you,
Ho-dee-ing-dong-doodle-all-a-day.

6

Geese in the pond and ducks in the ocean,
Ho-dee-ing-dong-doodle-all-a-day.
Devil's in the women when they take a notion,
Ho-dee-ing-dong-doodle-all-a-day.

7

Old gray goose goin' down the river,
Ho-dee-ing-dong-doodle-all-a-day.
If I'd been a gander I'd a-went with her,
Ho-dee-ing-dong-doodle-all-a-day.

Old Joe Clarke

*Arrangement
by Elie Siegmeister*

I used to live on moun - tain top, But now I live in town. I'm
board - ing at the big hot - el, Court - ing Bet - sy Brown.

Chorus

Fare you well, old Joe Clarke Fare you well I'm gone.

Fare you well, old Joe Clarke, Good-bye, Bet - sy Brown,

2

The funniest thing I ever saw
Was two old women fighting
The one cried out: "It's no fair fight!"
The other one's a-biting."
CHORUS: Fare you well, etc.

3

When I was a little girl
I used to play with toys;
But now I am a bigger girl
I'd rather play with boys.
CHORUS: Fare you well, etc.

4

When I was a little boy
I used to want a knife;
But now I am a bigger boy
All I want is a wife.
CHORUS: Fare you well, etc.

5

Once I had a muley cow
Muley when's she's born;
Took a buzzard a thousand years
To fly from horn to horn.
CHORUS: Fare you well, etc.

6

Wish I was a sugar tree,
Standing in the middle of some town—
Ev'ry time a pretty girl passed,
I'd shake some sugar down.
CHORUS: Fare you well, etc.

7

Old Joe Clarke had a yellow cat
She would neither sing nor pray;
She stuck her head in a buttermilk jar
And washed her sins away.
CHORUS: Fare you well, etc.

OLD JOE CLARKE

ROBERT W. GORDON describes in his article, "Some Mountain Songs from North Carolina," how he recorded tunes like "Old Joe Clarke."

"Long ago, even before you arrived, word of your coming has been spread. 'A furriner on his way up to Shelton's. Your recording phonograph and banjo have proclaimed you as ostensibly a 'musicioner' . . . Hardly have the first notes of the banjo sounded before they begin to appear. . . . At first it will be a bit hard to induce any one to play or sing for the phonograph, but once they have heard the living voice come back nothing can stop them. . . . One of the fiddlers and your host with the banjo have begun to play 'Old Joe Clarke.' Already two of the younger couples are dancing. The fiddler swings and sways as he plays. Your host begins singing the time-honored words his voice is rising sharp and clear above the music. As he comes to the chorus all join in."

Cindy

*Arrangement
by Elie Siegmeister*

lively

I wish I was an ap - ple, a - hang-in' in the tree, And

ev' - ry time my sweet-heart passed, she'd take a bit of me. She

told me that she loved me, she called me sug - ar plum, She

throwed 'er arms a - round me, I thought my time had come.

Get a - long home Cin - dy, Cin - dy, Get a - long home Cin - dy, Cin - dy,

Get a - long home Cin - dy, Cin - dy, I'll mar - ry you some time.

CINDY

"OLD TIMERS" believed that dancing to the fiddle or banjo was tanta-
mount to reserving a seat in Hell. But many of the mountain youngsters
like Cindy, just couldn't keep their feet virtuous when the twang of
the banjo was heard.

Cindy got religion, had it once before,
when she heard my old banjo, she 'uz the first one on the floor.

2

She took me to the parlor, she cooled me with her fan,
She swore that I's the purtiest thing in the shape of mortal man.
Oh where did you get your liquor, oh where did you get your dram?
I got it from a nigger, away down in Rockingham.
CHORUS: Get along home, etc.

3

Cindy got religion, she had it once before,
When she heard my old banjo, she 'uz the first one on the floor.
I wish I had a needle, as fine as I could sew,
I'd sew the girls to my coat tail, and down the road I'd go.
CHORUS: Get along home, etc.

4

Cindy in the springtime, Cindy in the fall,
If I can't have my Cindy girl, I'll have no girl at all.
Cindy went to the preachin', she swung around and around,
She got so full of glory, she knocked the preacher down.
CHORUS: Get along home, etc.

Darling Cora

*Arrangement
by Elie Siegmeister*

Go dig a hole in the mead-ow, Go dig a hole in the ground. Go dig a hole in the mead-ow, Let me lay dar-ling Cor-ie down.

down.

2
The first time I saw darling Corie,
She was standing on the banks by the sea,
With a .44 buckled around her,
And a banjo on her knee.

3
Go away, go away, darling Corie,
And do and best you can
I will get me another woman,
And you can get you another man.

4
The last time I saw darling Corie,
She had a .44 in her hand,
Kill that revenue officer,
That took away her man.

5
Go away, go away, darling Corie,
Quit your hanging around my bed.
Whiskey has ruined my body,
Pretty woman has killed me stone dead.

Ground Hog

Arrangement
by Elie Siegmeister

At a Good Clip, Tangy

Shoul-der up your gun and call your dog,

Shoul-der up your gun and call your dog, A - way to the woods to

mf

simile

1st and others ✳ *last*

catch a ground hog, Ground hog.

✳ *Play Interlude once after every four or five verses; or as often as de-sired*

212

The fiddle-

WHAT WERE the boar-hunts of classical antiquity, the riding-to-hounds
of the gentry of England, or the exploits of Teddy Roosevelt in darkest
Africa, compared to this epic of the Kentucky mountains?

Two in the cleft and one in the log,
Two in the cleft and one in the log,
See'd his nose, Lord, I thought I knew it was a hog.
Ground hog.

Sam cocked his gun and Dave pulled the trigger,
Sam cocked his gun and Dave pulled the trigger,
But the one killed the hog was old Joe Digger.
Ground hog.

They took 'im by the tail and wagged 'im to a log,
They took 'im by the tail and wagged 'im to a log,
And swore by gosh! he's a hell of a hog!
Ground hog.

Up stepped Sam with a snigger and a grin:
Up stepped Sam with a snigger and a grin:
"Whatcha goin' to do with the groun' hog skin?"
Ground hog.

Scrapes 'im down to his head and feet,
Scrapes 'im down to his head and feet,
By damn, Sam, here's a fine pile o' meat!
Ground hog.

They put 'im in the pot and all begin to smile,
They put 'im in the pot and all begin to smile,
They eat that hog before he struck a bile.
Ground hog.

Hello, mama, look at Sam,
Hello, mama, look at Sam,
He's eat all the hog 'n' a-soppin' out the pan!
Ground hog.

Watch 'im, boys, he's about to fall,
Watch 'im, boys, he's about to fall,
He's eat till his pants won't button at all.
Ground hog.

Careless Love

*Arrangement
by Elie Siegmeister*

Love, oh love, oh care - less love,

Love, oh love, oh care - less love, Oh it's love, oh love, oh

care - less love You see what care - less love has done.

2

Once I wore my apron low,
Once I wore my apron low,
Oh it's once I wore my apron low
You'd follow me through rain and snow.

3

Now I wear my apron high,
Now I wear my apron high,
Oh it's now I wear my apron high,
You'll see my door and pass it by.

CARELESS LOVE

THE CLASSIC Southern version of an—alas!—eternal theme. The same motif appears in the Blues song, "Every night when the Sun Goes In," and W. C. Handy was the first of a series of composers who have turned "Careless Love" to account in more sophisticated versions.

4

I cried last night and the night before,
I cried last night and the night before,
Oh I cried last night and the night before
Going to cry tonight and cry no more.

5

How I wish that train would come,
How I wish that train would come,
Oh it's how I wish that train would come
And take me back where I come from.

6

I love my mama and papa too,
I love my mama and papa too,
Oh I love my mama and papa too
But I'd leave them both to go with you.

7

It's on this railroad track I stand,
It's on this railroad track I stand,
Oh it's on this railroad track I stand
All for the love of a railroad man.

John Hardy

Arrangement
by Elie Siegmeister

JOHN HARDY

SOME FOLK BALLADS arise out of fantasy and imagination, but many, if not most, are narratives based on actual happening. For some time John Hardy, the hero of this ballad, was thought to be a symbolic or legendary character, sometimes confused with John Henry. But a few years ago a diligent searcher showed that the Negro bad man had actually lived in West Virginia, that the incidents recounted in the ballad had a solid foundation in fact.

John Hardy worked for the Shawnee Coal Company. He murdered a man in an argument over a crap game, was caught after a chase, convicted and hanged in the town of Welch, McDowell County, West Virginia, on January 19, 1894. His story was made into a ballad, which spread into many states and is still sung to-day.

2

ohn Hardy was a-standing by the dark sea bar,
e was unconcerned in the game,
 yeller gal threw down a fifty cents, sayin',
Deal John Hardy in the game," po' boy, sayin',
Deal John Hardy in the game."

3

ohn Hardy stepped up with the money in his hand,
aying, "I have money to play.
n' the one who wins this yeller gal's money,
 have powder to blow him away!" Lord, Lord!
 have powder to blow him away!"

4

he cards was dealt an' the money on the board,
ave Campbell won that twenty dollar bill.
ohn Hardy drew his pistol, an' he took sure aim an' fired,
n' he caused Dave Campbell's brains to spill, Lord, Lord!
le caused Dave Campbell's brains to spill!

5

ohn Hardy had twelve miles to go,
n' six of them he ran,
le ran till he came to the river bank,
hen he fell on his bosom an' he swam, Lord, Lord!
le fell on his bosom an' he swam.

6

John Hardy went to this big, long town,
When he thought he was out of the way,
Up stepped a marshal and taken him by the hand,
Says, "Johnny, come and go with me," po' boy,
Says, "Johnny, come and go with me."

7

John Hardy had a father and mother,
He sent for them to go his bail.
No bail was allowed for murderin' a man,
So they shoved John Hardy back in jail, po' boy,
So they shoved John Hardy back in jail.

8

Johnny Hardy was standin' in his cell,
With the tears runnin' down his eyes,
"I've been the death of many a poor man,
And now I'm ready to die, O Lord,
And now I'm ready to die.

9

"I've been to the east and I've been to the west
I've been this wide world round,
I've been to the river and I've been baptised,
So take me to my hanging ground, O Lord,
So take me to my hanging ground."

Kentucky Moonshiner

Arrangement
by Elie Siegmeister

Rather Slow but Freely

I've been a moon-shin-er for sev'n-teen long years. I've spent all my mon-ey on whis-key and beers. I'll go to some hol-ler, I'll put up my still, I'll make you one gal-lon for a two dol-lar bill.

KENTUCKY MOONSHINER

THE TANG AND DESOLATENESS of the lonely ridges is well portrayed in this nostalgic melody, with its overtones of good times enjoyed in solitude. The scoops and slides, the free intonation, the indefinite floating rhythm of the tune, are in characteristic mountain style.

2

I'll go to some grocery and drink with my friends.
No women to follow to see what I spends.
God bless those pretty women, I wish they were mine.
Their breath smells as sweet as the dew on the vine.

3

I'll eat when I'm hungry and drink when I'm dry.
If moonshine don't kill me I'll live till I die.
God bless those moonshiners, I wish they were mine.
Their breath smells as sweet as the good old moonshine.

Rye Whiskey
(CLINCH MOUNTAIN)

Arrangement
by Elie Siegmeister

RYE WHISKEY
(Clinch Mountain)

THIS RIBALD, unbuttoned refrain paints an alluring picture in mountain imagery of what happens after the first gallon of apple-jack or corn likker has gone down. Here is a Bacchanal atop Clinch Mountain that compares favorably with the classic doings on the Brocken on Walpurgisnacht, and with what happened during that famous Night on Bald Mountain. Certainly old Bacchus could have asked for nothing better than to be a duck at the bottom of a whiskey ocean.

2

I'll eat when I'm hungry
And drink when I'm dry;
If whiskey don't kill me
I'll live till I die.

CHORUS:
Oh whiskey, rye whiskey,
I know you of old;
You rob my poor pockets
Of silver and gild.

3

If the ocean was whiskey
And I was a duck,
I'd swim to the bottom
And never come up.

CHORUS:
Oh whiskey, rye whiskey,
How sleepy I feel,
Oh whiskey, rye whiskey,
How sleepy I feel.

4

For work I'm too lazy
And beggin's too low,
Train robbin's too dangerous,
To gambling I'll go.

Repeat first chorus.

5

I'll tune up my fiddle
And rosin my bow
And make myself welcome
Wherever I go.

Repeat first chorus.

6

I've no wife to quarrel with,
No babies to bawl,
The best way of livin'
Is no wife at all.

Repeat first chorus.

Everybody's Welcome

Arrangement
by Elie Siegmeister

Eve - ry bo - dy's wel - come Yes, yes, wel - come! Eve - ry bo - dy's wel - come, To the dy - ing Lamb! Oh Glo - ry! Free Sal - va - tion! Oh Glo - ry! To the dy - ing Lamb.

From L. L. McDowell's *Songs of the Old Camp Ground*, published by Edwards Brothers, Inc.

Rise and Shine

Arrangement
by Elie Siegmeister

Oh Death

Arrangement
by Elie Siegmeister

What is this that I can see, Cold i-cy hands tak-ing hold of me. For death has come you all can see Hell-gate is op-en wide for me O death! O death! Can't you spare me o-ver for a-no-ther year?

OH, DEATH!

THERE ARE many in the mountains of Kentucky, who, while they are unable to read or write, know their Bible from cover to cover and can cite many a passage entire, both chapter and verse. This is the country where baptism is still by total immersion, where the pious gather in windowless log cabin churches for foot-washing rituals. It is in this region that the story is told of the preacher who ignored the Lord's call to preach, and was stricken and laid out for dead. But, stirring, he rose, stiff and cold, and begged the Lord to spare him in these stark and impressive lines.

2

I'll lock your jaws till you can't talk
I'll bind your legs till you can't walk.
I'll close your eyes so you can't see.
I'll bring you unto me.
Oh, death! oh death!
Can't you spare me over for another year?

9. The Old Chizzum Trail

THE ENDING of the Civil War released new energies for pushing further and completing the big job of the century: the opening of the Far West. The two decades following the conclusion of peace were the golden years of frontier adventure, when the last wild places were finally brought under control. While polite cosmopolitan novelists were mourning the passing of the age of romance, a generation of skilful, swaggering, hard-working fellows were living the experiences that were soon to be so romantically described in hundreds of dime novels and avidly followed by millions of small boys.

The 1870's and 1880's were the heyday of the cowboy. But while the Indian fights, train robberies, mail coach hold-ups and wild revels in clapboard saloons abound in the minds of Hollywood script writers, there were other realities in the cowboy's life: long days at the southern end of an endless herd of cows, choking hot prairie dust; long, cold sleepless hours of night-herding; unheroic losses of arm or leg in the crush of a thousand stampeding cattle; and, as the song tells us,

> . . . *bacon and beans 'most every day;*
> *I'd as soon be eatin' prairie hay.*

Opening up a huge country, in which any state was larger than two or three European countries, was a job which needed thousands of tough, raw-boned and careless men who could live hard and work harder. The West asked no passports and the men came from everywhere: from played-out farms and barren city streets; from jails and office desks. There were sailormen tired of the sea, and mountain boys who found it hard to grow corn on rocky hillsides. English, Irish, Negroes, Scandinavians, Germans, Czechs and Bulgarians, they came. They rode the round-ups and bedded cows down, and became American cowboys.

It was in the '60's and '70's that the railroads pushed through to Kansas and the grass began to be worn down on the old Chisholm Trail, the long drive from the Texas and Arkansas ranches up to the railroad shipping points and to the good grazing lands of Montana and Wyoming. John Lomax tells that between 1870 and 1890 one million mustang ponies were driven up the trail, along with twelve million head of cattle in herds of 1000 and 3000. The weeks and months on horseback on the long drive offered little to relieve the heat, the rain, the monotony, except thoughts of a grand bust-up to come at Dodge City—and song. Not all cowboys sang, nor did those who did sing pour out tunes one after another, as on a radio program. But often the jogging, loping, cantering rhythms of the horse would mold to a new pattern the flowing measures of a ballad or music hall tune remembered from the East, from Kentucky, from Ireland, or from the fo'c'sle of an ocean tramp. Cow calls, "ti yi's," "yeas," and "yippees," would fit into the musical scheme or form a new chorus to an old verse, and a cowboy song was in the making. Like the men who sang them, they came from everywhere, and made one grand jumble of styles. Yet the prairie life did something to them all, brought a distinctive color, a special accent, and a new subject matter: a unique style was born. Does it matter what the great-grandparents were of "Good-bye, Old Paint," or "The Night-Herding Song?" They are as pure-bred American as the comic strip, the buffalo nickel, or second generation Irish or Scandinavians.

Cowboy songs were often of a very practical nature. Those with sharp rhythmic cries were used to rally a sluggish herd; those with quiet rolling rhythms served as cattle lull-abies, "to drown the wild sound" of coyotes or other animals which could startle nervous herds and might provoke a disastrous stampede. Other songs were sung around the camp-fire to pass the long night hours on the trail: of desperadoes, bucking bronchos, noble and not-so-noble love songs ("I Gave My Girl a Quarter," etc.). These songs were vociferous, sentimental, braggart and self-pitying.

Besides the cowboys, there were others who helped push the frontier back: lumberjacks and railroad men. Why songs should grow up around certain occupations and not others is sometimes hard to say, but in this case, isolated living in closely bound-up groups certainly played an important role. Life in the deep woods, cut off from the world for months at a time by winter snows, brought with it the same community feeling as existed on the old ranches.

Professional lumbering—that is, cutting timber for sale—migrated from Maine through Pennsylvania to Minnesota and Wisconsin. Its greatest heyday came in the '70's and '80's, and with it the flowering of the shantyboy songs. Like those of the cowboy, the shanty-boy songs are rambunctious and sentimental, tough and tearful in turn. The lumberjack had his hardships and dangers, too: broken legs and heads from falling trees, log jams on icy rivers, hard-headed bosses who forget to pay off when the snows were gone. On long winter nights, around the big-bellied stove, no one was more welcome than the shanty-boy minstrel—often Irish or Negro, as among shanty singers at sea. The shanty-boy singer would sing of it all in his own rough-hewn verses, using some old vaudeville or ballad tune, or, if they would not fit, a tune of his own making.

These old shanty-boy songs, many of them collected by Franz Rickaby on his long treks through the timber country just before lumbering became mechanized and changed into a large-scale industry, have the bleak, lone-some quality of the dark woods. Although still sung here and there by a few old-timers, their glory has gone with the work of the husky, raw-boned laughing boys who gave life to them forty and fifty years ago.

But for all the work of the cowboys and lumberjacks, it was the railroad men who really completed the picture of opening the West. Driving millions of spikes down into the sun-baked prairie, they brought with them the songs of the iron horse that soon were to drown the sound of the other songs. To those who have eyes and ears for the present as well as the past, the locomotive is as mythical and romantic a figure as any Minotaur of antiquity. The energy, the speed, the sense of creative power that those men who bridged the trackless wilds felt; the washouts, the wrecks, the train robberies—all are portrayed in the work-songs of the trackmen and the ballads of the boys who rode the caboose. To the railroad man, the locomotive is not an "it"; it is a "he" or a "she" who can be coaxed, cajoled and thundered at. She can be sung to in cooing tones, or bellowed at in a hoarse voice when passing the wrong switch. Railroad songs are the animal ballads of an age of coal and steel, and when the rails bridged the country the rhythm of the wheels and the song of the whistle replaced the plod-ding ballads of mule-drivers and the loping refrains of horsemen.

Railroad songs are Irish, German, Negro and Southern, as are the men who work in the roundhouse or sit up in the cab. They are an indispensable part of the ballad history of our country and their humor and fantasy, even in this age of miraculously streamlined flyers, are testimony to the fact that the machine does not always crush the humanity out of men, but can sometimes add to it very much indeed.

The Chisholm Trail

Arrangement
by Elie Siegmeister

Well, come a-long boys and list-en to my tale, I tell you of my trou-bles on the old Chish-olm Trail. Co-ma-ti-yi-you-py, yap-py yay, yap-py yay, Co-ma ti-yi you-py yap-py yay.

2

My feet are in the stirrups and my rope is at my side,
Show me a hoss that I can't ride.

CHORUS: Coma ti yi youpy, etc.

3

I'm up in the mornin' before daylight,
And before I sleep the moon shines bright.

CHORUS: Coma ti yi youpy, etc.

OLD CHISHOLM TRAIL

THE SONG of the Chisholm trail is the cowboy classic; its simple beating tune; its forthright couplets; its 'Comma-ti-yi-youpy'; its extemporaneous yelps, whoops and yips; its occasional departures from singing into shouting, are as exciting as the clatter of horses' hooves on the hard prairie," says Margaret Larkin in "Singing Cowboy."

4

Oh! it's bacon and beans 'most every day,
I'd as soon be a-eatin' prairie hay.

CHORUS: Coma ti yi youpy, etc.

5

My slicker's in the wagon and I'm gettin' mighty cold,
And these long-horned sons-o-guns are gettin' hard to hold.

CHORUS: Coma ti yi youpy, etc.

6

I'll ride my horse to the top of the hill,
I'll kiss that gal, gol darn, I will.

CHORUS: Coma ti yi youpy, etc.

7

I went up the boss to draw my roll,
He had it figgered out I was nine dollars in the hole.

CHORUS: Coma ti yi youpy, etc.

8

I went up to the boss and we had a little chat,
I slapped him in the face with my big slouch hat.

CHORUS: Coma ti yi youpy, etc.

9

Oh, the boss says to me, "I'll fire you,
Not only you, but the whole damn crew."

CHORUS: Coma ti yi youpy, etc.

10

I'll sell my outfit just as soon as I can;
I won't punch cattle for no damn man.

CHORUS: Coma ti yi youpy, etc.

11

Goin' back to town to draw my money,
Goin' back home to see my honey.

CHORUS: Coma ti yi youpy, etc.

12

Well I'll sell my saddle and I'll buy me a plow,
And I'll swear begad, I'll never rope another cow.

CHORUS: Coma ti yi youpy, etc.

13

My seat is in the saddle and my saddle's in the sky,
An' I'll quit punchin' cows in the sweet bye and by

CHORUS: Coma ti yi youpy, etc.

I Ride an Old Paint

*Arrangement
by Elie Siegmeister*

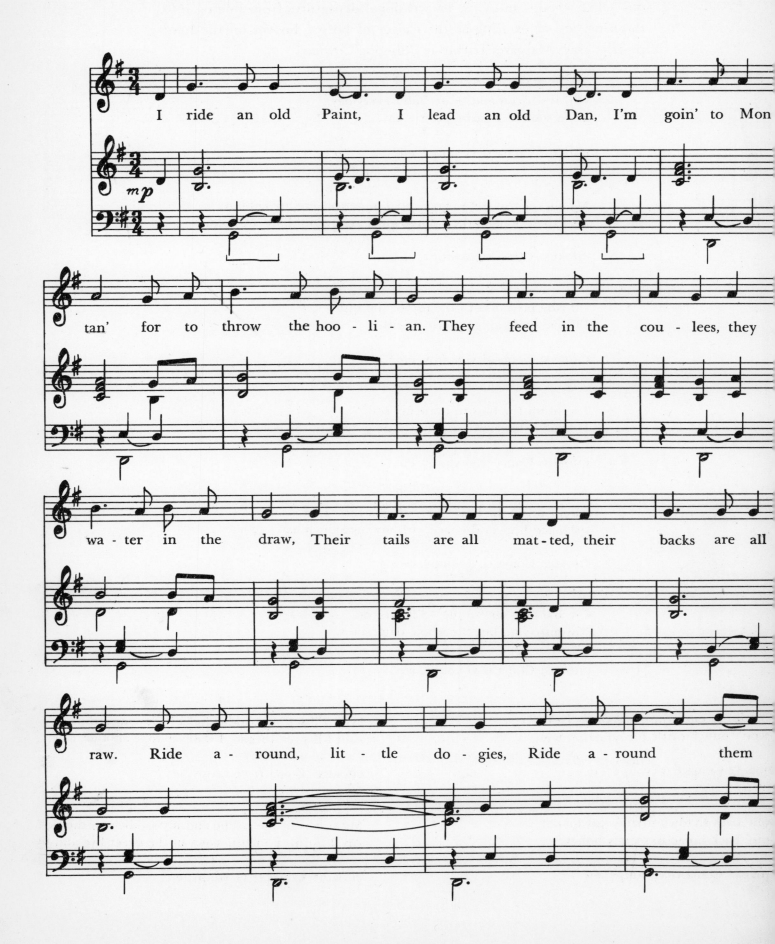

I ride an old Paint, I lead an old Dan, I'm goin' to Mon tan' for to throw the hoo - li - an. They feed in the cou - lees, they wa - ter in the draw, Their tails are all mat - ted, their backs are all raw. Ride a - round, lit - tle do - gies, Ride a - round them

slow, For the fie - ry and snuf - fy are a - rar - in' to go.

2

Old Bill Jones had two daughters and a song.
One went to Denver and the other went wrong.
His wife she died in a poolroom fight,
Still he sings from mornin' till night.
CHORUS: Ride around, etc.

3

Oh, when I die, take my saddle from the wall,
Put it on my pony, lead him out of his stall.
Tie my bones to his back, turn our faces to the West,
And we'll ride the prairie that we love the best.
CHORUS: Ride around, etc.

I RIDE AN OLD PAINT

COWBOYS WERE a hard-bitten lot, but the toughest frequently revealed a
tender streak. There is touching sentiment in the picture of this bucko's
bones riding west "on the prairie that we love best." A coulee is a de-
pression in the prairie; a draw, almost a ravine.

The Railroad Corral

*Arrangement
by Elie Siegmeister*

We're up in the morn-ing ere break-ing of day, The chuck wag-on's bus-y, the flap-jack's in play, The herd is a- stir ov-er hill- side and vale, With the night rid-- ers crowd-ing them in-to the trail.

2

Come take up your cinches, come shake out your reins,
Come wake your old broncho and break for the plains.
Come roust out your steers from the long chapparal,
For the outfit is off to the railroad corral.

RAILROAD CORRAL

A JOYFUL TUNE, sung when nearing the goal of the long, dusty trip up
the trail. The railroad corral was the point at which the cattle were
shipped, and after weeks, or sometimes months of following, guarding,
pacifying them, the cowboys were glad to see their charges on the way
to the stockyards. The rhythm of the song is that of galloping. Chapparal is a growth of low, thorny shrubs; cinch, a saddle girth.

3

The sun circles upward, the steers as they plod
Are pounding to powder the hot prairie sod
It seems, as the dust makes you dizzy and sick,
That we'll never reach noon, and the cool shady creek.

4

So tie up your kerchief and ply up your nag
Come, dry up your grumbles, and try not to lag;
Come on with your steers from the long chapparal,
We're far on the road to the railroad corral.

5

Come, shake out your rawhide and snake it up fair;
Come, break your old broncho to take in his share;
Come from your steers in the long chapparal,
For 'tis all in the drive to the railroad corral.

6

But the longest of days must reach evening at last,
The hills all climbed, the creeks all past.
The tired herd droops in the yellow light;
Let them loaf if they will, for the railroad's in sight.

Good-bye, Old Paint

*Arrangement
by Elie Siegmeister*

Good - bye, old Paint, I'm a - leav - ing Chey - enne; Good

bye, old Paint, I'm a - leav - ing Chey - enne; I'm a-

leav - ing Chey - enne, I'm off to Mon - tan' Good

bye, old Paint, I'm a - leav - ing Chey - enne.

GOOD-BYE OLD PAINT

A GOING-AWAY SONG in the persistent rhythm of a loping horse, it leaves
us wondering why this cowboy was so intent on "a-leavin' Cheyenne."
"Old Paint" was often used as a "good-night" song at cowboy dances,
something like the familiar "Good-night, ladies." Tradition had it that
as long as anyone remembered another verse, the dance still went on.

2

Goodbye, old Paint, I'm a-leaving Cheyenne;
Goodbye, old Paint, I'm a-leaving Cheyenne;
Old Paint's a good pony, he paces when he can;
Goodbye, old Paint, I'm a-leaving Cheyenne.

3

Goodbye, old Paint, I'm a-leaving Cheyenne;
Goodbye, old Paint, I'm a-leaving Cheyenne;
Go hitch up your hosses and give them some hay,
And seat yourself by me so long as you stay.

4

Goodbye, old Paint, I'm a-leaving Cheyenne;
Goodbye, old Paint, I'm a-leaving Cheyenne;
My hosses ain't hungry, they won't eat your hay,
My wagon is loaded and rolling away.

5

Goodbye, old Paint, I'm a-leaving Cheyenne;
Goodbye, old Paint, I'm a-leaving Cheyenne;
My foot's in the stirrup, my bridle's in my hand;
Good morning, young lady, my hosses won't stand.

Bury Me Not on the Lone Prairie

Arrangement
by Elie Siegmeister

"O bury me not on the lone prairie,
Where the wild coyotes will howl o'er me,
In a narrow grave just six by three;
O bury me not on the lone prairie!

BURY ME NOT

THIS CLASSIC of the plains has been harmonized, parodied, yodeled by so many college, bar-room and radio quartets that the "lone prair-ee" has become the cliché of every synthetic cowboy song and singer. Yet the original "Bury Me Not" has genuine pathos, desolation and the cynicism of tough-skinned men. It is sung to several melodies. Choice among them is difficult.

"O bury me not on the lone prairie,
Where the wild coyotes will howl o'er me,
Where the buzzard beats and the wind goes free;
O bury me not on the lone prairie!

"O bury me not on the lone prairie,
In a narrow grave six foot by three,
Where the buffalo paws o'er a prairie sea;
O bury me not on the lone prairie!

"O bury me not on the lone prairie,
Where the wild coyotes will howl o'er me,
Where the rattlesnakes hiss and the crow flies free;
O bury me not on the lone prairie!

"O bury me not," and his voice failed there,
But we took no heed of his dying prayer;
In a narrow grave just six by three
We buried him there on the lone prairie.

Cowboy's Gettin' Up Holler

*Arrangement
by Elie Siegmeister*

Rather Slow but Freely

Wake up, Ja - cob, day's a- break- in', Fry- in' pan's

on an' hoe- cake bak- in'. hot.

JOHN A. LOMAX tells us this call is frequently heard in western camps. On Southern chain gangs, the caller sings out, "Wake up, boys, spit on a rock," or, "Wake, snakes, day is breakin'." All these calls may have come from or given birth to the line in that old spiritual.
"Wake up Jacob, day's a-breakin'."

Wake up, Jacob, day's a-breakin',
Fryin' pan's on an' hoe-cake bakin'.

Bacon in the pan, coffee in the pot;
Git up now and git it while it's hot.

The Erie Canal

Arrangement
by Elie Siegmeister

I've got a mule, her name is Sal,— Fif - teen years on the
Er - ie Can - al. She's a good old work - er and a good old pal,
Fif - teen years on the Er - ie Can - al. We've hauled some barg - es

in our day, Filled with lum-ber, cod and hay—And eve-ry inch of th

way I know From Al - ba - ny to Bu - ffa - lo.

Chorus

Low Bridge, ev - ery bo - dy down, For it's Low Bridge We're

com - ing to a town! You can al - ways tell your neigh - bor, You can

al - ways tell your pal, If you've ev - er nav - i - gat - ed on the

1.
E - rie Ca - nal.

2.
E - rie Ca - nal.

ERIE CANAL

FOR YEARS the Erie Canal served as the main artery of communication and trade between the Atlantic Ocean and the Great Lakes. Between Albany and Buffalo, "Lumber, coal and hay" and a hundred other commodities flowed in a never-ending stream. The canal boat mule-drivers in their pull past the "inland towns with the sea-going names"—Brockport, Middleport, Gasport, Lockport—found relief in cadences molded by the tedium of the long haul. Carl Carmer relates that "riders on the slow canal boats got many a bruised cranium from failing to heed the warning cry of the 'hoggie' or mule driver—'Low Bridge, Everybody Down.'"

The Shantyman's Life

Arrangement by Elie Siegmeister

Moderately lively

Oh a shan-ty man's life is a wear-i-some life Al-though

some think it void of care   Swing-ing an ax from

morn-ing till night, In the midst of the for-ests so drear.

Ly - ing in the shan - ty bleak and cold While the cold storm - y

wint - ery winds blow, And as soon as the day - light

doth ap - pear, To the wild woods we must go.

But when spring it does set in, double hardships then begin,
When the waters are piercing cold,
And our clothes are dripping wet and fingers benumbed,
And our pike-poles we scarcely can hold.
Betwixt rocks, shoals and sands give employment to all hands
Our well-banded raft for to steer,
And the rapids that we run, oh they seem to us but fun,
For we're void of all slavish fear.

The Wreck of the Old 97

Arrangement
by Elie Siegmeister

Moderately Lively

He was hand-ed up his or - ders at Mon - roe, Vir - gin - ia, say - ing

"Steve you're way be - hind time. This is not thir - ty-six, but

old nine - ty- se - ven, You must get her in - to Spen - cer on time."

2

Steve Rooklyn turned to his old black fireman
Said, "Shovel on more coal,
For when we hit that old White Mountain
You can see old Ninety-seven roll."

WRECK OF THE OLD 97

"ON A SEPTEMBER DAY thirty-six years ago No. 97, the fast mail train of the Southern Railway between Washington and Atlanta, was dashing along the eastern slopes of the Blue Ridge Mountains of Virginia. Leaving Lynchburg late, the engineer, Joe Brodie, opened the throttle as the train raced down the steep grade of the White Oak Mountain near Danville. But the pace was too fast, and at a curving trestle the flier left the rails, plunging into the ravine, destroying the equipment and killing most of the crew.

"The catastrophe became so famed in song that . . . (it was) sung for years in country gatherings, in wayside taverns, and on street corners in Virginia and North Carolina towns."—*New York Times, November 13th, 1939.*

The Victor Talking Machine Company sold more than 1,200,000 records of "The Wreck of the Old 97," making a profit of $130,000.00. It was forced to pay part of this to David Graves George who proved he had written the balled in 1903, to the music of "The Ship That Never Returned."

3

It's a long rough road from Lynchburg to Danville
And it's down a three-mile grade;
It was down that grade that he lost his air brakes—
You can see what a jump he made.

4

He was comin' round a turn doing ninety miles an hour,
When his whistle began to scream, (toot-toot)
He was found in the wreck with his hand on the throttle:
He was scalded to death by the steam.

5

Now lady, oh lady, take fair warning
From this time and now on;
Never speak harsh words to your true and loving husband,
He may leave you and never return.

10. On the Job

COMMON FOLK know what it means to "sing for your supper." The Minnesota reaper, the Maine teamster, the hand laying rails in the desert, the youngster working a push-boat up a Tennessee River, the New Orleans dock-hand, have found the need to sing at or about their work. Sometimes happy, sometimes bitter, sometimes laughing and sometimes strictly practical, these songs tell the story of the adventures and hardships of the many people whose hands have shaped the destiny of this country.

In this country it is the Negro who has made the widest use of the group work-song. The tradition goes back to plantation days when, moving steadily down rows of cotton, breaking rocks on a mountain road, or toting bales on the levee, large groups of slaves would lift their voices and bodies in unison under the rhythmic guidance of a leader. After Emancipation the work-song tradition persisted and grew among southern railroad gang laborers.

Natalie Curtis Burlin vividly describes a typical "Hammering Song":

"In the mines of Virginia this 'Hammerin' Song' chimed with the ringing of the hammer as the men chanted the . . . refrain which gave rhythm and pace to monotonous toil. The improvised verses were usually started by the 'header' or headman, who received extra pay for his good voice, his quick musical fancy and his ability to keep the men singing and thus working in unison. 'An' as soon as we'd git started a-*singin'*,' a Negro explained, 'We'd forgit we was ti-yerd, an' so long as the header would keep de song a-goin', we'd keep ohn a-hammerin' an' a-*hammerin'*!'

". . . Usually it is the leader who sings alone, for the worker must keep his lungs full while swinging the heavy hammer. Yet sometimes the men break into harmony, joining in after the first words . . . and it is just this extraordinary fusion of the rhythm of men's toiling bodies with the beat of music that makes the work-chants of the Negro typical. . . ." *

The conditions of group work in the outdoors thus gave rise not only to the typical harmonized style of the Negro work-song, but also to elements of that special type of singing recently talked about as "hot intonation." Isolated from contact with city-made and city-tuned instruments, the Negro singer developed a more flexible type of intonation based on the natural scale, intermingled with quarter tones, slides, grunts, shouts, sharp "hanhs"—violent exhalations of breath accompanying the descent of the hammer or pickaxe—and with an absolutely unique musical quality. All these colors of the Negro work-song were taken over and amplified into the Blues, Jazz and into the "hot" playing of Sidney Bechet and Louis Armstrong.

Because of its striking choral form, the work-music of the Negroes has received ample and deserved attention, which has, however, tended to obscure the songs of the white American worker. These have tended to be individual songs *about* work, not necessarily sung on the job, but at almost any time. Except in the case of the old sea shanties, there is little evidence that the white worker ever sang in gangs. At the beginning, Americans were a footloose people, not bound to the soil, rarely, in the early days, tied down for long to any one spot. In consequence, his songs of work had nothing of the fixity of an established style about them, but took on the characteristics of a shifting, migrating people.

* From Book IV of the Hampton Series of "Negro Folk Songs."

Carl Sandburg has compared the Erie Canal Song to the Song of the Volga Boatmen. In spirit, maybe—but in form what a world of difference. The Russian song, so steady, fixed in its measures, is the work chant of chained prisoners, serfs bound for life to one job and to one endless plodding pace. The tune of the "Canawllers," with its shifting syncopation, its ennobled ragtime pulse is the song of men free to come and go, to change from one job to another, picking up music hall strains on the way. So other work-songs have given and taken motifs from the minstrels, from vaudeville, from old ballads, from spirituals. The fascinating hybrids that resulted make for much of the charm of American work-music.

While in the hammering or cotton-picking song, whose main function is to set the pace for work movements, the rhythm is the main factor and the verses are often a sequence of half-remembered, patched together phrases, often making very little sense, in the ballad that tells about work, the text is of major importance. Every man knows most intimately the hardships and annoyances of his own particular job, and it is never the sailor who sings, "Oh, for a life on the ocean wave!" Song is an ideal outlet for unspoken grievances, and it is not surprising that the sharecropper sings of the voracious boll weevil, the boatman of a strong current, the mill worker of meager income, and the prisoner of the hardship of cracking rocks.

One peculiarly American job not usually thought of in musical terms is that of the promotion man. The technique of modern advertising, with its streamlined use of musical motifs as radio theme songs for gasoline, soap, and breakfast foods, had its forerunners in the Hamlin musical troupes who toured the length and breadth of the land, drawing crowds to their Wizard Oil spiels by singing humorous and sentimental songs. More direct musical salesmanship may be found in the song cries of street peddlers from Brooklyn to New Orleans, that are familiar to every housewife. And more often than not, the peddler with the best cry will have the best sales.

The songs and ballads of Americans on the job are powerful, trivial, gay, sarcastic, and matter-of-fact by turns. They reveal to us much about the plain day-to-day feelings of millions of average, day-to-day people. They stand as a lyric testimony to the imagination and creative power of the men who built the nation.

Look Over Yonder

Words and Music
by Lawrence Gellert

Arrangement
by Elie Siegmeister

Look o - ver yon - der, huh, Hot burn - ing sun turn - ing
o - ver, Look o - ver yon - der, huh, Hot burn - ing sun turn - ing
o - ver, And it won't go down. Oh my Lord, it won't go down.

2

I was a-hamm'ring, huh,
Hamm'ring away last December.
I was a-hamm'ring, huh,
Hamm'ring away last December.
Wind was so cold,
Oh my Lord, wind so cold.

LOOK OVER YONDER

THIS TYPICAL ROCK-PILE SONG from a Georgia prison is harsh and eloquent with toil. Gangs of Negroes will chant rhythmical refrains like this for hours, as they work. The fall of the hammer is accompanied by the sharp exhalation "hunh!" which marks the pulse of the song.

3
Can't you all hear them, huh,
Cuckoo birds all a-holl'ring.
Can't you all hear them, huh,
Sure sign of rain,
Oh my Lord, sure sign of rain.

4
My little woman, huh,
She keep sending me letter,
My little woman, huh,
She keep sending me letter.
Don't know I'm dead
Oh my Lord, don't know I'm dead.

5
Sometimes I wonder, huh,
Wonder if other people wonder.
Sometimes I wonder, huh,
Wonder if other people wonder.
Just like I do,
Oh my Lord, just like I do.

Farmer Comes to Town

Arrangement
by Elie Siegmeister

When the farm-er comes to town with his wag-on brok-en down, Oh, the farm-er is the man who feeds them all. If you'll on-ly look and see, I think you will a-gree That the farm-er is the man who feeds them all. The farm-er is the man, the farm-er is the man,

Lives on cred-it till the Fall. With the in-terest rate so high, it's a won-der he don't die, For the mort-gage man's the one who gets it all.

When the banker says he's broke, and the merchant's up in smoke,
They forget that it's the farmer feeds them all.
It would put them to the test if the farmer took a rest;
Then they'd know that it's the farmer feeds them all.

The farmer is the man, the farmer is the man,
Lives on credit till the Fall;
And his pants are wearing thin, his condition it's a sin,
He's forgot that he's the man who feeds them all.

The Ballad of the Boll Weevil

Arrangement
by Elie Siegmeister

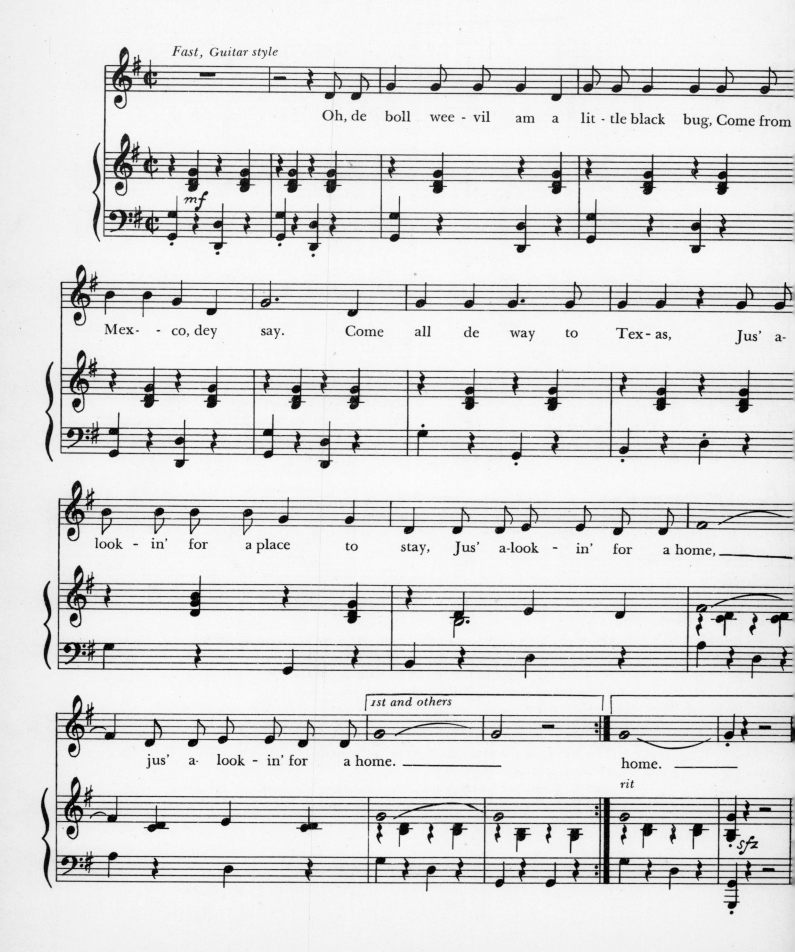

Oh, de boll wee-vil am a lit-tle black bug, Come from Mex--co, dey say. Come all de way to Tex-as, Jus' a-look-in' for a place to stay, Jus' a-look-in' for a home, _____ jus' a- look-in' for a home. _____ home. _____

1st and others

BALLET OF THE BOLL WEEVIL

"The boll weevil is a promising subject for balladry, since he furnishes many romantic motifs. He is an outlaw, hunted in every field. He has apparently superhuman powers of resistance to hardship, exposure, and attacks from man, the individual, and from organized society. He has an extraordinary cunning and trickery, can outwit and flout man, and go his way despite all human efforts to outwit him." *

    * Dorothy Scarborough: "On the Trail of Negro Folk Songs."

This "ballet" is sung so widely throughout the cotton states that it might be considered the theme song of the Southern share-cropper.

2

De first time I seen de boll weevil,
He was settin' on de square.
De next time I seen de boll weevil,
He had all of his fam'ly dere,
Jus' a-lookin' for a home, jus' a-lookin' for a home.

3

De farmer take de boll weevil,
An' he put him in de hot san';
De weevil say, "Dis is mighty hot,
But I'll stand it like a man.
Dis'll be my home, dis'll be my home."

4

De farmer take de boll weevil
An' he put him in a lump of ice.
De weevil say to de farmer,
"Dis is mighty cool an' nice,
Dis'll be my home, dis'll be my home."

5

De boll weevil say to de farmer,
"You can ride in dat Fohd machine,
But when I get through wid yo' cotton
Can't buy no gasoline.
Won't have no home, won't have no home."

6

De merchant got half de cotton,
De boll weevil got de res'
Didn't leave de farmer's wife
But one ol' cotton dress,
An' it's full of holes, an' it's full of holes.

7

De farmer say to de merchant,
"We's in an awful fix,
De boll weevil et all de cotton up
An' left us only sticks.
We go on home, we go on home."

8

De farmer say to de merchant,
"I want some meat an' meal."
"Get away from here, you son of a gun,
You got boll weevils in yo' fiel',
Goin' to get yo' home, goin' to get yo' home."

9

De farmer say to de merchant,
"We ain't made but only one bale,
And befoh we'll give you dat one,
We'll fight and go to jail,
We'll have a home, we'll have a home."

Shine On

Words and Music
by Luke Schoolcraft

Arrangement
by Elie Siegmeister

Lively Dance Rhythm

My ole mas-sa prom-ised me, Sing a lit-tle hoe-down Jor-dan, When he died he set me free. Oh! Jer-u-sa-lem. My ole mas-sa nev-er die at all, Sing a lit-tle hoe-down Jor-dan,

Wizard Oil concert troupes toured the country in wagons, stopping in town squares to regale the populace with the latest minstrel songs, humorous and sentimental ditties. "Shine On," one of the perennial favorites of the Hamlin troupes, retailed the lament of the slave who despaired of winning freedom, since:

DURING THE 1880's, when the stream-lined techniques of modern advertising were as yet unborn, the Hamlin Wizard Oil Company was pioneering in new methods of parting man from his money. Their oil, of course, was guaranteed to cure every ailment from Cholera Morbus to flat feet.

The Shoemaker

Arrangement
by Elie Siegmeister

Lively, Cheerful

I am a shoe- mak- er by my trade, I'll work in rain- y weath- er, Be- sides two pair I've made to- day Of a side and a half of leath - er.

Chorus

Whack de loo- de-dum, Whack de loo- de-doo- de Whack de loo- de-dum, Kate, you are my darl ing. darl ing.

1st and others *last*

256

11. Big Men and Bad Men

WRITERS HAVE told us the age of fantasy, of myths, legends and giants is dead. Possibly in many countries it is. But if we look at the story of our own land—not as written in history books, but as told in the speech, tales and songs of Americans who made the country —we find fantasies wilder than any ever before dreamed of; fairy tales and giants more colossal than any ever imagined; demons who tamed the lightning, harnessed the whirlwind and took the tornadoes in tow. Carl Carmer in his fascinating book, "The Hurricane's Children," pointed out that American fairy tales, unlike those of practically any other country, do not deal at all with the "little people," with elves, pixies, brownies or fairies. They are all about *big* people, whose footprints when filled with water make the Great Lakes; whose hammer-strokes make the mountains ring; whose lassos rope a thousand steers at one throw.

Wise men tell us that the myths and legends of a people symbolize their unconscious dreams and aspirations. In our case, there was nothing unconscious about it; the land was big and wild, the dream of clearing it, taming it, making it habitable was gigantic, heroic.

Davy Crockett, one of those frontiersmen who were "half horse, and half alligator, and the rest snapping turtle," told bigger whoppers, about grinning coons crazy, or grinning the knots off trees; of a muley cow so big "it took a buzzard a thousand years to fly from horn to horn." But the biggest whopper of all was Davy himself, getting elected to Congress as a prank, fighting the Indians, then sticking up for them in Washington, singing, "Won't You Come into My Bower?" as he picked off advancing Mexicans at the Alamo.

Says Carmer:

"At the end of a hard day's work the American cowboys or miners or lumberjacks or applepickers have had their fun out of making up stories about men who could do jobs that just could not be done, in an impossibly short time, with one hand tied behind them."

Such a story was the yarn that must have come after a long rainy spell in the North woods about Paul Bunyan who got caught in a rain so thick that water-spouts reached right up into the sky. He jumped in one, swam up it until he reached the top, and turned it off.

Kemp Morgan, Mike Fink, Febold Feboldson, Tony Beaver, Johnny Appleseed—these were the heroes of a race of movers and doers, of a people that finds no job too big, no odds too great to be taken and licked. From one of them Carl Sandburg culled that classic phrase: "We'll fight till hell freezes over, and then write on the ice, 'Come on, you b - - - - - ds!'".

With bigness comes simplicity. Thomas Jefferson, who believed in that fantastic thing, democracy, enough to make it work, received the British ambassador in his bedroom slippers. Abraham Lincoln, according to the story, would have entertained the politicians, bankers and clergymen, who were to swing the Presidential nomination for him, in similar fashion had it not been for the prompt and efficacious intervention of his wife.

These are the men who symbolize America, who live in the hearts of the people, in story and in song. Then there are legendary figures who grow out of the doings of real men: the tale of a crazy apple-planter who turned the Ohio Valley from an empty wilderness to a garden of apple-trees. Johnny Appleseed was the male Ceres or Demeter of a race of Yankee planters. There is the immortal saga of man against the machine, of his death-struggle and symbolic victory: the giant John Henry, about whom songs have grown abundantly. Then there is the music of villains and desperadoes, from the diamond-studded stock market juggler, Jim Fisk, to those western bandits like Sam Bass, Billy the Kid and Jesse James, who "robbed from the rich to give to the poor."

Each of these in his time lived out a real life on earth. But in song they became not one but many men, they became all men, all Americans. No more fantastic than the Kentucky pioneers, the Mississippi River captains, the '49ers rounding Cape Horn, of the past, or those Americans of today who sit through the whole Antarctic winter, follow a solar eclipse down to Central Africa, or spend thirty years in a laboratory tracking down a microbe no one has yet heard of, they tell us more of the spirit in which this country was conceived and brought into being than all the history books, political speeches and newspaper editorials put together.

Old Abe Lincoln

*Arrangement
by Elie Siegmeister*

Old Abe Lin - coln came out of the wild - er - ness,

Out of the wild - er - ness, out of the wild - er - ness, Old Abe Lin - coln came

out of the wild - er - ness, Many long years a - go.

ALTHOUGH HE HAD RISEN to the highest office any American can attain,
to the people in the backwoods, the dwellers in the swamps and to those
who roamed the canebreak the man in the tall top-hat and frayed shawl
was still "Old Abe" who came out of the wilderness.

Jeff Davis tore down the government,
down the government, tore down the government,
Jeff Davis tore down the government,
long years ago.

But old Abe Lincoln built up a better one,
Built up a better one, built up a better one,
Old Abe Lincoln built up a better one,
Many long years ago.

Johnny Appleseed

Lyrics
by Rosemary Benet

Music
by Elie Siegmeister

Johnny Apple-seed! Johnny Ap-ple-seed!

Of Jon-a-than Chap-man two things are known: That

he loved ap-ples, that he walked a-lone. At sev-en-ty odd he was

gnarled as could be, But rud-dy and sound——— as a good ap-ple

tree. For fif-ty years o-ver of har-vest and dew,

He plan-ted his ap-ples where no ap-ples grew. The

winds of the prai-rie might blow thru his rags, But he car-ried his seed

Johnny Appleseed

*Lyrics
by Rosemary Benet*

*Music
by Elie Siegmeister*

in deer skin bags. ___ John-ny Ap - ple seed! John-ny

Ap - ple - seed! John-ny Ap-ple- seed! ___

2

From Ashtabula to Fort Wayne,
He planted and pruned and planted again.
He had no hat to encumber his head,
He wore a tin pan on his white hair instead.

A fine old man as ripe as a pippin,
His heart still light, and his step still skipping
He nested with owl, with bear cub and possum,
And knew all his orchards, root, tendril and blossom.

Johnny Appleseed! Johnny Appleseed!

JOHNNY APPLESEED

"IN 1806 Johnny Appleseed had expanded his operations. Down the Ohio he went, with two boats lashed together, bearing apple seed. Stopping here and there, wherever he found settlers, he started a little nursery. From the Ohio he branched off into the Muskingham, and thence up the White Woman Creek, and into the Mohican, and into the Black Fork. Later with his seeds in leather bags on his back, he tramped the trail from Fort Duquesne to Detroit by way of Fort Sandusky, starting nurseries all along the line. Thus for more than half a century Johnny Appleseed went just ahead of the oncoming farms with his little nurseries from which they could get trees, through Ohio, into Indiana, to Fort Wayne. A hundred thousand miles of the Northwest he thus provided with orchards."

From Marjorie Barstow Greenbie's "American Saga"

3

The stalking Indian, the beast in its lair,
Did no hurt while he was there,
For they could tell, as wild things can,
That Jonathan Chapman was God's own man.

Why did he do it? We do not know
He wished that apples might root and grow.
He has no statue, he has no tomb,
But he has his apple trees still in bloom.

Johnny Appleseed! Johnny Appleseed!

I have always thought there must be a song somewhere about this unique character of American history and folk lore. Not finding any, I wrote one.

E. S.

Casey Jones

*Arrangement
by Elie Siegmeister*

Come all you round-ers if you want to hear A
cal - ler called Cas - ey at a half past four,

stor - y of a brave En - gin - eer, Cas - ey Jones was the
Kissed his wife at the sta - - - tion door, Mounted to the cabin with his

round - er's name, On a six eight wheel - er, boys, he
orders in his hand, And he took his fare - well trip to that

2

Put in your water and shovel in your coal,
Put your head out the window, watch them drivers roll,
I'll run her till she leaves the rail,
'Cause I'm eight hour late with that western mail.
He looked at his watch and his watch was slow,
He looked at the water and the water was low,
He turned to the Fireman and he said,
"We're going to reach Frisco but we'll all be dead."

CASEY JONES

IN AN ERA of coal and steel, Casey Jones is the romantic figure who sits in the railroad cab and guides his train around hairpin curves through fog, snow, landslides, blizzards. Throughout the South, Casey Jones is the symbol of all heroic engineers who stick it out and die at the end of the line.

Casey really lived, and is said to have died in a wreck in 1909, fourteen miles north of Canton, Mississippi. The tragedy was almost immediately translated into song by some unknown Negro, and soon spread far and wide throughout the South. Two travelling vaudevillians, Newton and Seibert heard some Negro boys in New Orleans singing one of the numerous versions. Realizing its commercial possibilities, they gave the song a ragtime twist and brought it to New York, where it became a hit.

There are many songs about train wrecks, but none like "Casey Jones."

CHORUS:
Casey Jones! Going to reach Frisco,
Casey Jones! But we'll all be dead.
Casey Jones! Going to reach Frisco—
We're going to reach Frisco, but we'll all be dead."

3
Casey pulled up that Reno hill,
He tooted for the crossing with an awful shrill,
The switchman knew by the engine's moan
That the man at the throttle was Casey Jones.
He pulled up within two miles of the place,
Number Four stared him right in the face,
Turned to the Fireman, said, "Boy, you'd better jump,
'Cause there's two locomotives that's a-going to bump."

CHORUS:
Casey Jones! Two locomotives!
Casey Jones! That's a-going to bump.
Casey Jones! Two locomotives!
There's two locomotives that's a-going to bump.

4
Casey said just before he died,
"There's two more roads that I'd like to ride."
Fireman said, "What could that be?"
"The Southern Pacific and the Santa Fe."
Mrs. Jones sat on her bed a-sighing,
Just received a message that Casey was dying.
Said "Go to bed, children, and hush your crying,
'Cause you got another papa on the Salt Lake Line

CHORUS:
Casey Jones! Got another papa!
Casey Jones! On that Salt Lake Line!
Casey Jones! Got another papa!
And you've got another papa on that Salt Lake Line

Jesse James

*Arrangement
by Elie Siegmeister*

Jes-se James was a lad who killed man-y a man. He robbed the Glen - dale train. He stole from the rich and he gave to the poor; He'd a hand and a heart and a brain. Poor Jes-se had a wife to mourn for his life; Three child-ren, they were

brave; But that dir - ty lit - tle cow - ard that shot Mis - ter How-ard Has laid poor Jes - se in his grave.

2

It was Robert Ford, that dirty little coward;
I wonder how he does feel,
For he ate of Jesse's bread and he slept in Jesse's bed,
Then laid poor Jesse in his grave.

CHORUS: Poor Jesse, etc.

3

Jesse was a man, a friend to the poor,
He never would see a man suffer pain;
And with his brother Frank he robbed the Chicago bank,
And stopped the Glendale train.

CHORUS: Poor Jesse, etc.

JESSE JAMES

"IF AMERICA ever had a Robin Hood, it was the bandit and train robber, Jesse James, whose life and death are celebrated in this ballad. . . . Like all thieves of folk lore, he was kind to the poor. Old Timers will tell you he always helped a fellow who was down on his luck." *Margaret Larkin: "Singing Cowboy"*

Shortly before his death, Jesse was living in retirement under the assumed name of "Mr. Howard." He was hanging a picture on the wall, when Robert Ford, a member of Jesse's gang, and a guest in his household, shot him from behind, for the sake of the reward. This is one of the very few ballads in which the author, in this case, one Billy Gashade, reveals his identity.

4

It was on Saturday night, Jesse was at home
Talking with his family brave;
Robert Ford came along like a thief in the night
And laid poor Jesse in his grave.

CHORUS: Poor Jesse, etc.

5

This song was made by Billy Gashade,
As soon as the news did arrive;
He said there was no man with the law in his hand
Who could take Jesse James when alive.

CHORUS: Poor Jesse, etc.

John Henry

*Arrangement
by Elie Siegmeister*

Listen to my story____ 'tis a story true;

'Bout a might - y man, John Henry was his name, And John

Hen - ry was a steel - driv - er too, Lawd, Lawd, John

Hen - ry was a steel - driv - er too.

JOHN HENRY

WHETHER JOHN HENRY ever really lived or is just a legend that came out of the hearts of his people, he is known, loved, and sung about by Negro workmen everywhere. Although there are some Negroes in the South who may not know the name of the President, there are few who cannot tell you the story of John Henry.

His ballad is sung in dozens of versions. They have him driving steel on the Air Line, the K. C., the Frisco, the C. and O. railroads; they call his woman Lucy, Delia Ann, Polly Ann; he is "sittin' on his pappy's knee" or holding his little son "in de palm of his han'." It is a seven-, and nine- or a ten-pound hammer that is the death of him. But on this they all agree: John Henry battled with the steam drill which threatened to "beat him down"; toiled mightily from dawn to sunset; beat the machine as the sun went down, and "died wid a hammer in his han'."

The dignity of this ballad, its color, its dramatic power mark it as one of the masterpieces of folk creation, as one of the most important American contributions to music.

2

John Henry had a hammah; weighed nigh fo'ty poun';
Eb'ry time John made a strike,
He seen his steel go 'bout two inches down, Lawd, Lawd,
He seen his steel go 'bout two inches down.

3

John Henry's woman, Lucy, dress she wore was blue;
Eyes like stars an' teeth lak-a marble stone,
An' John Henry named his hammah "Lucy" too, Lawd, Lawd,
An' John Henry named his hammah "Lucy" too.

4

Lucy came to see him, bucket in huh han';
All the time John Henry ate his snack,
O Lucy, she'd drive steel lak-a man, Lawd, Lawd,
O Lucy, she'd drive steel lak-a man.

5

One day Cap' Tommy told him how he'd bet a man;
Bet John Henry'd beat a steam-drill down,
Jes' 'cause he was th' best in th' lan', Lawd, Lawd,
Jes' 'cause he was th' best in th' lan'.

John Henry, tol' Cap' Tommy, lightnin' in his eye;
"Cap'n bet you las' red cent on me,
Fo' I'll beat it to th' bottom or I'll die," Lawd, Lawd,
Fo' I'll beat it to th' bottom or I'll die."

Co'n pone's in my stomach, hammah's in my han',
Hain't no steam-drill on dis railroad job
Can beat "Lucy" and her steel-drivin' man, Lawd, Lawd,
Can beat "Lucy" and her steel-drivin' man.

Sun shined hot an' burnin', wer'n't no breeze at-tall;
Sweat ran down like watah down a hill
That day John Henry let his hammah fall, Lawd, Lawd,
That day John Henry let his hammah fall.

John Henry kissed his hammah, white man turned on steam;
Li'l Bill held John Henry's trusty steel,
'Twas th' biggest race th' worl' had ever seen, Lawd, Lawd,
'Twas th' biggest race th' worl' had ever seen.

White man tol' John Henry, "Niggah, damn yo' soul,
You might beat dis steam drill o' mine
When th' rocks in this mountain turn to gol'," Lawd, Lawd,
"When th' rocks in this mountain turn to gol'."

John Henry tol' th' white man, tol' him kind-a sad,
"Cap'n George, I want-a be yo' fr'en;
If I beat yo' to th' bottom, don' get mad," Lawd, Lawd,
"If I beat yo' to th' bottom, don' get mad."

Cap' Tommy sees John Henry's steel a-bitin' in;
Cap'n slaps John Henry on th' back,
Says, "I'll give yo' fifty dollars if you win," Lawd, Lawd,
Says, "I'll give yo' fifty dollars if you win."

White man saw John Henry's steel agoin' down;
White man says, "That man's a mighty man,
But he'll weaken when th' hardes' rock is foun'," Lawd, Lawd,
"But he'll weaken when th' hardes' rock is foun'."

14

John Henry, O John Henry, John Henry's hammah too;
When a woman's 'pendin' on a man
Hain't no tellin' what a mighty man can do! Lawd, Lawd,
Hain't no tellin' what a mighty man can do!

15

John Henry, O John Henry, blood am runnin' red!
Falls right down with his hammah to th' groun'
Says, "I've beat him to th' bottom but I'm dead," Lawd, Lawd,
Says, "I've beat him to th' bottom but I'm dead."

16

John Henry kissed his hammah, kissed it with a groan,
Sighed a sigh an' closed his weary eyes,
Now po' Lucy has no man to call huh own, Lawd, Lawd,
Now po' Lucy has no man to call huh own.

17

Lucy ran to see him, dress she wore was blue;
Started down th' track an' she nevah did turn back,
Sayin', "John Henry I'll be true—true to you," Lawd, Lawd,
Sayin', "John Henry I'll be true—true to you."

18

John Henry, O John Henry, sing it if yo' can,
High an' low an' ev'rywhere yo' go,
He died with his hammah in his han'! Lawd, Lawd,
He died with his hammah in his han'!

12. Heart Throbs and Monkeyshines

Warm from my Breast surcharg'd with grief
& Woe,
These Melancholy Strains spontaneous flow.

The grand leap of a whale . . . up the falls of Niagara is esteemed, by all who have seen it, as one of the finest spectacles in nature.

Thus did Benjamin Franklin, over one hundred and eighty years ago, apply two formulas that have come to be the mainstay of the American entertainment industry ever since: powerful sentiment and tall-story nonsense. From the early colonial broadside ballads and tavern singers through the minstrel shows, on through the works of Mark Twain, the early nickelodeon shows, Will Rogers and the comic strip to the latest Cream of Mush radio program, the combination of home, mother, love and parting, with outrageous punning, gagging, pie-throwing, darn-fool humor, has invariably tugged at the American heart and purse-strings. Politicians get elected to office by mastering its technique: Abe Lincoln won over the constituents of Sangamon County by using it in his front door speeches. Salesmen with their foot in the door always try it; lawyers work it on case-hardened juries; even doctors cure patients by first making them laugh and then saying, "Do it for the sake of the old folks!"

American hearts have always beaten indignantly at the story of the poor orphan child, the whipped horse, the faltering steps of the homeless wanderer, the deceived maiden. But at the proper moment they have always been able to execute a lightning switch to the most outrageous parodies of the same.

John Hill Hewitt tells of one of the renditions in 1839 of that throbbing classic, "Wood-man, Spare That Tree" by its composer, Henry Russell:

"He had finished the last verse. . . . The audience was spell-bound for a moment, and then poured out a volume of applause that shook the building to its foundation. In the midst of this tremendous evidence of their boundless gratification, a snowy-headed gentleman, with great anxiety depicted in his venerable features, arose and demanded silence. He asked, with a tremulous voice: "Mr. Russell, in the name of Heaven, tell me, was the tree spared?' 'It was, sir,' replied the vocalist. 'Thank God! Thank God! I breathe again!' and then he sat down, perfectly overcome by his emotions." *

A few years later, students at New York University were singing, to the same tune, "Oh Barber, Spare Those Hairs!"

Audiences have wept to many another refrain, whose very titles today are enough to moisten an uninhibited eye: "The Old Arm Chair," "Oh, No, We Never Mention Her," "The Brave Old Oak," "Those Locks, Those Ebon Locks," "Rock Me to Sleep, Mother," "The Lost Letter," "She Sleeps in the Valley," and "The Inebriate's Lament." And then, shortly afterwards they devoured such elegant tomfoolery as "Root Hog or Die," "Kafoozalem," "Throw Him Down, McCloskey," "Abdul the Bulbul Ameer," and "You Never Miss the Water Till the Well Runs Dry."

Perhaps the haywire, monkeyshine spirit was the necessary antidote to too much weepy close harmony of the lavendar-and-lace days. At any rate, it is only necessary to turn on the radio to realize that both still reign in the American soul. And when the high-powered symphonic passion of the latest studio ar-

* Quoted by J. T. Howard in "Our American Music."

rangements and the fabricated smartness of the quick-paced gag songs have begun to pall, it might be time to switch off the knobs and drift back to "Darling Nelly Gray," "Go Get the Axe," "The Elephant and the Flea," and many another immortal classic.

Red River Valley

*Arrangement
by Elie Siegmeister*

CHORUS:

Come and sit by my side if you love me,

Do not hasten to bid me adieu,

But remember the Red River Valley

And the girl that has loved you so true.

RED RIVER VALLEY

EVERY ONCE in a while a little known folk tune is "discovered" by some Broadway tunesmith and turned into a Tin Pan Alley or concert favorite. "Itiskit, Itaskit" and "Short'nin' Bread" are two recent examples that come to mind. Sometimes the opposite happens: the people take for their own a current Broadway favorite, and turn it into a folk song. A generation ago the New York song, "In the Bright Mohawk Valley" spread throughout the South and the West, where the name of the stream was changed to Red River. Although long since forgotten on Broadway, it has become the permanent property of folks in rural districts throughout the country.

2

Won't you think of the valley you're leaving?
Oh how lonely, how sad it will be,
Oh think of the fond heart you're breaking,
And the grief you are causing me?

CHORUS: Come and sit, etc.

3

I have promised you, darling, that never
Will a word from my lips cause you pain;
And my life, it will be yours forever
If you only will love me again.

CHORUS: Come and sit, etc.

Darling Nelly Gray

Words and Music
by B. R. Hanby

Arrangement
by Elie Siegmeister

There's a low green val-ley on the old Ken-tuck-y shore, There I've whiled man-y hap-py hours a-way, A sit-ting and a-sing-ing by the lit-tle cot-tage door, Where lived my darl-ing Nel-ly Gray.

Oh! my poor Nel - ly Gray, they have tak - en you a - way, And I'll
ne - ver see my darl - ing an - y more. I'm a-sit - ting by the riv - er and I'm
weep -ing all the day, For you've gone from the old Ken - tuck - y shore.

One night I went to see her but "she's gone" the neighbors say,
The white man bound her with his chain,
They have taken her to Georgia for to wear her life away,
As she toils in the cotton and the cane.

CHORUS: Oh! my poor Nelly Gray, etc.

Listen to the Mocking Bird

*Words and Music
by Alice Hawthorne*

*Arrangement
by Elie Siegmeister*

val - ley, _____ The val - ley, _____ the val - ley, _____ She's

sleep - ing in the val - ley _____ And the mock - ing bird is sing - ing where she lies.

List - en to the mock - ing bird, List - en to the mock - ing bird, The

mock - ing bird, still sing - ing o'er her grave; List - en to the

mock - ing bird, List- en to the mock - ing bird,
Still sing - ing where the weep - ing wil - lows wave.

2

Ah well I yet remember,—
Remember,—remember,—
Ah! well I yet remember—
When we gathered in the cotton side by side.
'Twas in the mild September,
September,—September,—
'Twas in the mild September—
And the mocking bird was singing far and wide.
CHORUS: Listen to the mocking bird, etc.

No More Booze

Arrangement
by Elie Siegmeister

There was a lit-tle man and he had a lit-tle can, And he
used to rush the grow-ler; He went to the sa-loon on a
Sun-day aft-er-noon, And you ought to hear the bar-ten-der hol-ler:

Chorus

No more booze, no more booze, No more booze on Sun-day;

No more booze, no more booze, Got to get your can filled

Mon - day. She's the on - ly girl I love, With a

face like a horse and bug - gy. Lean - ing up a - gainst the

lake, O fire - man! save my child!

NO MORE BOOZE!

IN THE LAST DAYS of the past century, long-sleeved, bustled ladies met in solemn conclave to determine how they might best win the vote and stamp out the curse of inebriation. It took several decades to achieve both goals, but at least one thing was effected: in some states laws were passed closing the saloons on Sundays. Hence the origin of the plaint (to be sung with pathos!) , "No more booze on Sunday!"

2

The chambermaid came to my door,
"Get up, you lazy sinner,
We need those sheets for table-cloths
And it's almost time for dinner."
CHORUS: No more booze, *etc*.

Little Brown Jug

Arrangement
by Elie Siegmeister

LITTLE BROWN JUG

THE GOLDEN GOBLET of the Gods, the bottomless horn of Norse mythology, the "beaker full of the warm South" spoken of by the poet, the costly wine-glass broken after every drink by the French aristocrat of tradition, can have contained no more ecstatic liquids than were held within the walls of the "little brown jug."

2

'Tis you who makes my friends and foes,
'Tis you who makes me wear old clothes,
Here you are so near my nose,
So tip her up and down she goes.

CHORUS: Ha! ha! ha! etc.

3

When I go toiling to my farm
I take little brown jug under my arm
Place him under a shady tree,
Little Brown Jug, 'tis you and me.

CHORUS: Ha! ha! ha! etc.

4

If all the folks in Adam's race
Were gathered together in one place
Then I'd prepare to shed a tear
Before I'd part with you, my dear.

CHORUS: Ha! ha! ha! etc.

5

If I'd a cow that gave such milk,
I'd clothe her in the finest silk,
I'd feed her on the choicest hay,
And milk her forty times a day.

CHORUS: Ha! ha! ha! etc.

6

The rose is red, my nose is, too,
The violet's blue and so are you;
And yet I guess, before I stop
I'd better take another drop.

CHORUS: Ha! ha! ha! etc.

It's the Syme the Whole World Over

Arrangement
by Elie Siegmeister

IT'S THE SYME THE WHOLE WORLD OVER

A MEANINGFUL MORSEL for maudlin moralists. Will also do to oil up
your rusty Cockney accent.

2

She was just a parson's daughter,
Pure, unstyned was 'er fyme;
'Till a country squire came courtin'—
And the poor girl lorst 'er nyme.

3

So she went aw'y to Lunnon,
Just to 'ide 'er guilty shyme.
There she met another squire;
Once agine, she lorst 'er nyme.

4

Look at 'im with all 'is 'orses,
Drinking champyne in 'is club,
W'ile the wictim of 'is passions
Drinks 'er Guinness in a pub.

5

Now 'e's in 'is ridin' britches,
'Untin' foxes in the chyse,
W'ile the wictim of 'is folly
Mykes 'er livin' by 'er wice.

6

So she settled down in Lunnon,
Sinkin' deeper in 'er shyme,
Till she met a lybor leader
And ag'yn she lorst 'er nyme.

7

Now 'e's in the 'ouse of Commons
Mykin' laws to put down crime,
W'ile the wictim of 'is plysure
Walks the street each night in shyme.

8

Then there cyme a bloated bishop.
Marriage was the tyle 'e told.
There was no one else to tyke 'er
So she sold 'er soul for gold.

9

See 'er in 'er 'orse and carriage,
Drivin' d'ily through the park.
Though she's myde a wealthy marriage
Still she 'ides a brykin' 'eart.

10

In a cottage down in Sussex
Lives 'er payrents old and lyme.
And they drink the wine she sends 'em.
But they never speaks 'er nyme.

11

In their poor and humble dwellin',
There 'er grievin' payrents live,
Drinkin' champyne as she sends 'em
But they never can forgive.

12

It's the syme the whole world over,
It's the poor what gets the blyme,
While the rich 'as all the plysures;
Now, a'nt that a blinkin' shyme!

Suckin' Cider Through a Straw

*Words and Music
by Carey Morgan and Lee David*

*Arrangement
by Elie Siegmeister*

The pret - ti - est gal   That ev - er I   saw,

Was* suck - in'   ci - - - der Through a   straw.

**In this song all "s"s and "c"s are to be sung with a pro-
tracted lisp, to portray a profound and heartfelt sip.*

2

I told that gal
I didn't see how
She sucked the cider
Through a straw.

3

And cheek by cheek
And jaw by jaw,
We sucked that cider
Through that straw.

4

And all at once
That straw did slip;
I sucked some cider
From her lip.

5

And now I've got
Me a mother-in-law
From suckin' cider
Through a straw.

13. The Wicked City

THE TURN of the century brought to an end the heroic days of the west. The endless frontier had been closed at last, and with it went the glamour and romance that made Jesse James and Billy the Kid material for newspaper headlines, novels, songs, and the dreams of small boys.

With the frontier days gone, the focus of theatrical, literary and musical attention shifted to the Big Bad City. It was the era of muckraking, suffragette parades, exposés of the big trusts, clean-up campaigns and anti-vice crusades. In the light of the gaslamps, long-sleeved, hour-glass-waisted ladies plied their nefarious trade, while eminent divines thundered against Sin and Corruption. Tammany was in its heyday, and emphatic reformers on soap-boxes cried out for the poor working girl. Temperance advocates wept, because for all their documentary evidence of the evils of alcohol, the law still provided for closing the saloons only on Sunday.

With themes such as these, the popular sheet-music business, which had always traded on sentiment, attained heights hitherto undreamed of. It was the era of soul-rending tragedies, of life-long shame produced by One Moment of Weakness. It was the day when many a throat choked with anguish to the rhythms of "The Fatal Wedding," "The Little Lost Child," "The Picture That Is Turned to the Wall," "The Moth and the Flame," "Just for the Sake of Our Daughter," "Only a Bird in a Gilded Cage," and "Take Back Your Gold." (Those without feeling will, of course, only scoff and sneer.)

It was "After the Ball" that broke all existing records for popular song-hits. Whether it was the Tragedy of the Fatal Misunderstanding, the Pathos of Eternal Regret, or the heroic sweep of the melody that did it, will remain a problem for the sociologist. Suffice it to say that "After the Ball" is the first song that comes to mind, together with "Sidewalks of New York" and "Daisy Bell," when one thinks of the naughty, gay, tearful old days of the horse-car when mother was young.

Meanwhile on the other side of the tracks, quite another type of music was growing up. The city had never been known as the birthplace of folk song, but the mauve decade was brewing a strange new brew. Out of dives, honky-tonks, waterfront emporiums and hop joints that provided an inexpensive if temporary release from the monotony of small town life and from work in mills or sweatshops; through the smell of stale beer and old smoke, came the strains of tunes that were to become rowdy American classics, that were destined to live on when the more made to order contemporary music hall epics of Purple Passion were long forgotten.

Where did the story of Frankie and the Man who Did her Wrong originate? There are many claimants. Some say the original Frankie still lives; others that her name wasn't Frankie at all, but Sadie, Josie, or Lil, and that Johnny's real name was Albert. We are told that he was shot with a forty-four, a Gatling gun, or with just a plain revolver. The song is reputed variously to have come from St. Louis, Cincinnati, the South, the Mountains.

All that we do know is that, together with "Willie the Weeper," "Cocaine Lil," and the "St. James Infirmary—or Gambler's—Blues," it was the start of a new, vigorous strain in native song. While the throats that gargled it out on the back alleys, might never have sung a scale, and the hands that pounded it on tinny pianos never known Czerny, the new "lowdown" style was genuine. Its language was

291

stark, colorful, straight from the shoulder. Its tunes were raucous and cheap, but strong. It was this barrel-house and honky-tonk concoction that with various other admixtures, was to evolve in two decades through rag-time and jazz to the liveliest most potent popular dance music Americans had ever made the world trip a foot to.

The Roving Gambler

*Arrangement
by Elie Siegmeister*

I am a rov-ing gam-bler, I've gam-bled all a-round, Wher-ev-er I meet with a deck of cards I lie my mon-ey down.

I've gambled down in Washington and I've gambled over in Spain;
I am on my way to Georgia to knock down my last game.

I had not been in Washington many more weeks than three,
Till I fell in love with a pretty little girl and she fell in love with me.

She took me in her parlor, she cooled me with her fan,
She whispered low in her mother's ears, "I love this gambling man!"

"O daughter, O dear daughter, how could you treat me so,
To leave your dear old mother and with a gambler go?"

O mother, O dear mother, I'll tell you if I can;
If you ever see me coming back again I'll be with the gambling man."

Frankie and Johnny

Arrangement
by Elie Siegmeister

Fran - kie and John - ny were lo - vers, Oh, Lor - dy, how they could

love! They swore to be true to each oth - er, Just as

True as the stars a - bove, He was her man,

but he done her wrong. wrong

FRANKIE AND JOHNNY

THIS MOST FAMOUS of American low-down songs is sung in three hundred different ways throughout the land. Who were these famous lovers, and where was the tragic story enacted? Some say that it happened in real life and that the original Frankie, now a woman of eighty, still lives in St. Louis. Others say she hailed from Cincinnati, San Francisco, Omaha, Seattle, the mountains.

2

Frankie and Johnny went walking,
Johnny in his brand new suit.
"Oh, good Lord," says Frankie,
"Don't my Johnny look cute."
He was her man, but he done her wrong.

3

Johnny said, "I've got to leave you,
But I won't be very long,
Don't you wait up for me honey,
Nor worry while I'm gone."
He was her man, but he done her wrong.

4

Frankie went down to the corner,
Stopped in to buy her some beer
Says to the fat bar-tender,
"Has my Johnny man been here?"
He was her man, but he done her wrong.

5

"Well I ain't going to tell you no story,
Ain't going to tell you no lie.
Johnny went by, 'bout an hour ago,
With a girl named Nellie Blye,
He was your man, but he's doin' you wrong."

6

Frankie went home in a hurry,
She didn't go there for fun,
She hurried home to get a-hold,
Of Johnny's shootin' gun.
He was her man, but he's doin' her wrong.

7

Frankie took a cab at the corner,
Says "Driver, step on this can."
She was just a desperate woman,
Gettin' two-timed by her man.
He was her man, but he's doin' her wrong.

8

Frankie got out at South Clark Street,
Looked in a window so high
Saw her Johnny man a-lovin' up,
That high brown Nellie Blye.
He was her man, but he's doin' her wrong.

9

Johnny saw Frankie a-comin',
Out the back door he did scoot,
But Frankie took aim with her pistol;
And the gun went "Root a toot-toot!"
He was her man, but he done her wrong.

10

"Oh roll me over so easy,
Roll me over so slow,
Roll me over easy boys,
'Cause my wounds they hurt me so.
I was her man, but I done her wrong."

11

Bring out your long black coffin,
Bring out your funeral clo'es,
Johnny's gone and cashed his checks,
To the grave-yard Johnny goes.
He was her man, but he done her wrong.

12

Drive out your rubber-tired carriage,
Drive out your rubber-tired hack;
There's twelve men going to the grave-yard,
And eleven coming back.
He was her man, but he done her wrong.

13

The sheriff arrested poor Frankie,
Took her to jail that same day
He locked her up in a dungeon cell,
And threw the key away,
She shot her man, though he done her wrong.

Willie the Weeper

*Arrangement
by Elie Siegmeister*

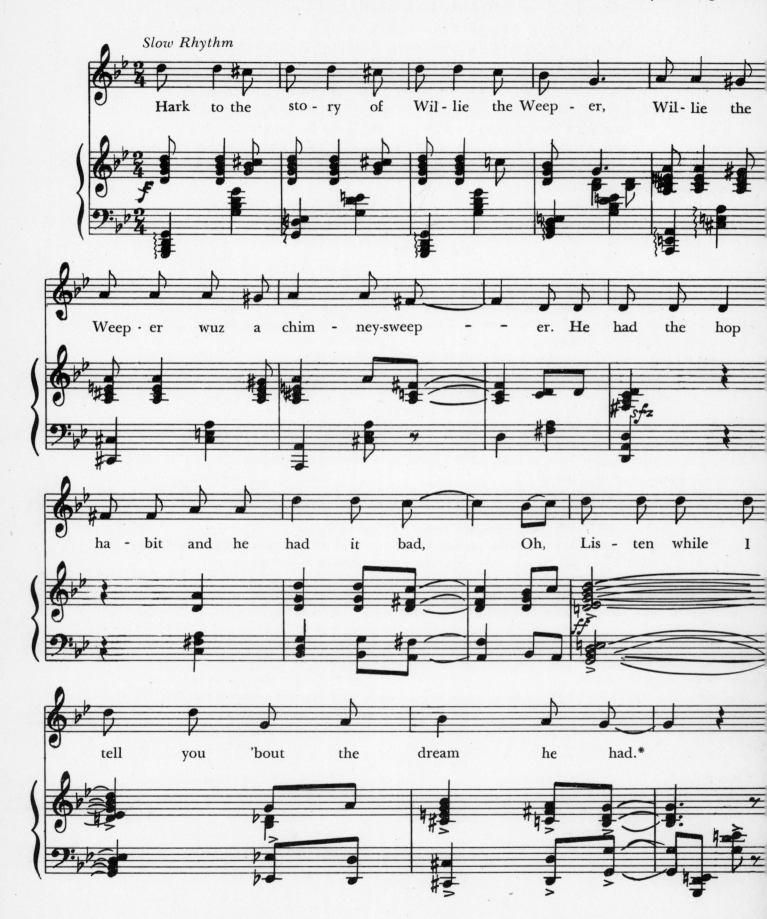

Slow Rhythm

Hark to the sto - ry of Wil - lie the Weep - er, Wil - lie the

Weep - er wuz a chim - ney-sweep - - er. He had the hop

ha - bit and he had it bad, Oh, Lis - ten while I

tell you 'bout the dream he had.*

WILLIE THE WEEPER

A LOW-DOWN epic of the coke-house. Broadway reincarnated Willie the Weeper as "Minnie the Moocher." After a temporary glory, Minnie died, but Willie still weeps. Floating through an ecstatic fantasy of un-inhibited adventures, he "plays poker with presidents, eats nightingale tongues a queen cooks for him . . . he lights his pipe with a hundred dollar bill, has heart affairs with Cleopatra, the Queen of Sheba and movie actresses." says Carl Sandburg.

2

He went to the hop-joint the other night,
When he knew that the lights would all be burning bright,
I guess he smoked a dozen pills or more,
When he woke up he wuz on a foreign shore.

3

Queen o' Bulgaria wuz the first hemet;
She called him her darlin' an' her lovin' pet.
She promised him a pretty Ford automobile,
With a diamond headlight an' a silver steerin'-wheel.

4

She had a million cattle, she had a million sheep;
She had a million vessels on the ocean deep;
She had a million dollahs, all in nickels an' dimes;
She knew 'cause she counted them a million times.

5

Willie landed in New York one evenin' late,
He asked his sugar for an after-date.
Willie he got funny, she began to shout:
Bim bam boo!—an' the dope gave out.

** Don't hesitate to add extra notes when needed or switch the
tune around as the spirit moves you for the various verses.*

14. The Melting Pot

THE EARLY SETTLERS in this country were Spanish, French, English, Irish, Swedes, Germans and Dutch. On the muddy streets of their primitive villages little boys and girls played games, and danced to songs in many different languages, among them "Malbrough s'en va t'en Guerre," "Ach, Du Lieber Augustin" and "Rosa, Willen Wy Dansen." After the British had gained mastery of the colonies of most of the other nations, children sang the same melodies, but now "Malbrough" had become "The Bear Went Over the Mountain"; "Augustin" became "Did You Ever See a Lassie?" and "Rosa, Willen Wy Dansen," "Rosa, Let Us Be Dancing."

Today, long after America has attained its own musical maturity, the same process of absorption and adaptation continues, with Neapolitan, Russian and Mexican folk melodies being transformed into popular radio favorites: "The Woodpecker Song," "Two Guitars," and "The Dove." Americans have always taken the cultural treasures brought over by the settlers of every nationality and added them to our national store. The successive waves of immigration which brought to these shores peoples of a score of different races and nationalities contributed greatly to the enrichment of our musical heritage. All the racial strains had their share in the development of our own indigenous music when, at length, it did develop. England and Scotland were responsible for the greatest number of ballads Africa and Ireland for the largest part of the minstrel songs (to which, however, even distant Poland added her bit *); while in the shaping of rag-time and jazz, Negro, Spanish, Hungarian, Jewish and French Creole influences are said to have had their share. It is significant that out of this

*See "Walk-jaw-bone."

most varied of mixtures has come the most characteristic of all American musical styles.

Musical strains have come to us not only from Europe, but from Spanish America as well. Cubans have brought the Rumba and the Conga (Americanized by Cole Porter in "Begin the Beguine"); South Americans, the Tango; Mexico has contributed such colorful and characteristic songs as "La Cucuracha" and "Cielito Lindo"; while the latest addition is the saucy West Indian style known as "Calypso."

While many of these national strains have become an integral part of the American musical language, others have retained their autonomous character, generally as a result of compact local settlements of fairly isolated language groups. This has been the case with the Slovaks and Poles in the Pittsburgh iron and steel area; with French-Canadians in Maine; with Mexicans in Texas and New Mexico, all of whom have retained their own native folk songs. In some cases these groups have developed a new style, based on a mixture of the traditional idiom with American influences. Such are the songs of New Orleans Creoles; of Jews in the sweatshops of New York and Chicago; of the Pennsylvania Dutch around Bethlehem, and the street cries of Italian peddlers in almost any big city.

In the field of classical music it is to the credit of many foreign born Americans, that they became the most ardent exponents of Americanism in music. Among these were the German, Father Heinrich, who in the 1830's went to Kentucky, lived with the Indians and was the first to write symphonic works with such titles as "Yankee Doodliad," "Pocahontas," and "The Pilgrim Fathers"; Louis Moreau Gottschalk, the son of an English Jew and a Creole mother, who was one of the first to utilize such native Negro dances as "The Banjo," the "Bamboula," and "Le Bananier" in larger works; the Irish-born Victor Herbert; the Hungarian-American, Sigmund Romberg; and the Bohemian-American, Rudolf Friml. And the most beloved of all modern American composers, George Gershwin, was born on New York's East Side, of Russian-Jewish parents.

Thus, reaching deeply into the fertile store of world culture, America has added new riches to that store.

Rémon

Arrangement
by Elie Siegmeister

300

REMON

"Sung to a simple dance called the "Coonjai" . . . when the "Coonjai" is danced, the music is furnished by an orchestra of singers, the leader of whom. . . . sustains the solo part, while the others afford him an opportunity, as they shout in chorus, for inventing some neat verse to compliment some lovely danseuse, or celebrate the deeds of some plantation hero. . . . The usual accompaniment, besides that of the singers, is that furnished by a skilful performer on the barrel-head drum, the jaw-bone and key."

Allem, Ware and Garrison:
Slave Songs of the U.S.(1867)

Schlof, Bobbeli

*Arrangement
by Elie Siegmeister*

Schlof, bob - be - li, schlof, Der Daw - di hiet die
Sleep, lit - tle one, sleep, Your dad - dy's watching the

schof, Die Mom - mi hiet die laem - cher In die grie - ne
sheep, Your mum - my guards the little lambs, In the sweet mead-

schwaemm - cher, Schlof, bob - be - li, schlof.
ow land, Sleep, lit - tle one, sleep.

SCHLOF, BOBBELI, SCHLOF

THE "PENNSYLVANIA DUTCH" who settled around Harrisburg, Lancaster, Bethlehem and Reading from a hundred to two hundred years ago still remember—and sing—the old German love songs, dances, children's songs, and lullabies, in their own special dialect, which is often a mixture of English and German. In parts of eastern Pennsylvania, and in this song, "father" is "dawdi" rather than "Vater"; "mother" is "mommie" rather than "Mutter."

Salangadou

Arrangement
by Elie Siegmeister

Sa - lan - ga - dou, _____ Sa - lan - ga - dou- _____
_____ Sa - lan - ga - dou _____ Sa - lan - ga - dou, _____

Co - té pi - ti fille la yé, Sa - lan - ga -
"Oh, where is my dar — ling gone?"

dou, _____ Sa - lan - ga - dou? _____

I Catcha Da Plenty of Feesh

*Arrangement
by Elie Siegmeister*

De Mexico Ha Venido

Arrangement
by Elie Siegmeister

DE MEXICO HA VENIDO

THIS TUNE IS Mexican not only in its characteristic folk humor, but in its peppery tune, which, like many of its kind, depends for its effect on a subtle inter-play of shifting rhythms.

2

And Barabas he says, "No, it's not on the level—
Let the old women go and marry the devil."
The devil he's not stupid, and straightway does cry
"Before I'd marry that kind, I'd rather die!"

SALANGADOU

THE NEGRO SLAVES brought to the French settlements in the Mississippi valley spoke a special dialect of their own, termed Creole. After the Louisiana Purchase they continued this patois and sang their characteristic native songs. Creole songs are quite different from those of the English-speaking Negro. They show the French influence, not only in their musical style, but in their frivolous and sarcastic subject matter. Some of them have a very simple folk quality, and convey a note of tenderness. Such is this song of a mother who has lost her little girl, "Salangadou."

On Meesh-e-gan

*Arrangement
by Elie Siegmeister*

Frainch-man he don't lak to die in de fall,

When de mairsh she am so full of de game

An' de lee - tle bool - frog he's roll ver - ra fat

An' de lee - tle moosh - rat. he's jus' de same.

ON MEESH-E-GAN

In the lumber-camps of Maine, Minnesota, Michigan, a familiar figure is the raw-boned French-Canadian lad. His songs are often French, but this one, in English, relating the hardships of the "beeg log drive" on "Meesh-e-gan" has a savor all its own.

2

Come, all you great beeg Canada man
Who want fin' work on Meesh-e-gan,
Dere's beeg log drive all troo our lan',
You sure fin' work on Meesh-e-gan.

3

When you come drive de beeg saw log,
You have to jump jus' lak de frog.
De foreman come, he say go sak,
You got in de watair all over your back.

4

P'rhaps you work on drive tree-four day,
You fin' dat drive dat she don' pay,
You go to Sag-e-naw right away,
Wait roun' tree-four day 'fore you get your pay.

5

Mebbe you stay in Sag-e-naw tree-four week,
You get de ague, you feel damn seek,
One ounce quinine, two pound cal-o-mel,
You tak all dose 'fore you got well.

6

Now you all great beeg Canada man
Who want fin' work on Meesh-e-gan,
Dere's great beeg snake all troo our lan'
You sure get bit on Meesh-e-gan.

Finnegan's Wake

*Arrangement
by Elie Siegmeister*

Tim Fin-ni-gan lived in Walk-er Street, An I-rish gen-tle-man might-y odd; He'd a beau-ti-ful brogue so rich and sweet, And to rise in the world he car-ried the hod. But you see, he'd a sort of tip-pling way, For the love of the liq-uor poor Tim was born; And to

help him on his work each day, He had a drop of the cray-thur ev-ery morn. With my phi-lal-loo, hub-ba-boo, whack hur-roo, boys, Did-n't we sing till our jaws did ache, And shout and laugh till all was blue · With the fun we had at Fin·ni-gan's wake.

FINNEGAN'S WAKE

IN REVOLUTIONARY TIMES, one American out of every ten was Irish-born, and millions more came over during the great waves of immigration in the mid-nineteenth century. It is not surprising that the rhythm and color of the Irish dance tune, the jig, the ballad, and love song, permeated so deeply into the body of our native song. The flavor of Ireland entered into such early American songs as "Jefferson and Liberty," "Paul Jones' Victory" and "The Hornet and the Peacock," continued in "Old Zip Coon," "Joe Bowers" and "When Johnny Comes Marching Home," and was still strong in the more recent "State of Arkansas" and "The Shoe-maker."

"Finnegan's Wake" (from which the title of James Joyce's recent novel was taken), a famous vaudeville tune, was widely sung in this country after the 1860's, and is still recalled by some old-timers.

2

One morning Tim was rather full,
His head felt heavy, which made him shake,
He fell from the ladder and broke his skull,
So they carried him home, himself to wake.
They tied him up in a nice clean sheet,
And laid him out upon the bed,
Wid a gallon of whiskey at his feet,
And a barrel of praties at his head.

CHORUS: With my, etc.

3

His friends assembled at the wake
Miss Finnigan call'd out for the lunch,
First they brought in tay and cake,
Then pipes, tobacco, and whiskey punch;
Biddy O'Brine began to cry,
Such a pretty corpse she never did see,
Arrah Tim Mavourneen why did you die?
"Ah! hould you gab," said Paddy McGree.

CHORUS: With my, etc.

4

Then Peggy O'Connor tuck up the job,
"Biddy," says she, "you're wrong, I'm sure,"
But Biddy gave her a pelt in the gob,
And we left her sprawling on the flure;
Oh! then the war did soon enrage!
'Twas woman to woman, and man to man,
Shillelagh law did soon engage!
And a row and a ruction soon began.

CHORUS: With my, etc.

5

Then Mickey Mollaney raised his head,
When a gallon of whiskey flew at him,
It missed, an' falling on the bed,
The liquor scatter'd over Tim;
Be-dad he revives, see how he rises,
And Timothy, rising from the bed,
Saying, "Whirl your liquor round like blazes!
Arrah! Gudaguddug, do you think I'm dead?"

CHORUS: With my, etc.

15. Modern Tunes: the '10's and '20's

Got nowhar to lay my weary head,
Oh my babe, got nowhar to lay my weary
head.

ABOUT 1910, a new and original type of American song was introduced in New York's Tin Pan Alley: the Blues. Whether it was because the new style corresponded to the need of the moment or because it provided a naïve but simple and direct personal expression in song, the Blues spread rapidly throughout the country. In the troubled years immediately following the first World War, the Blues style was taken abroad, where it immediately proved to be as infectious as in this country.

Soon people were singing the Blues in Paris, London, Rome, Calcutta and Tokyo. In a dozen different countries, internationally known composers, among them Honegger, Ravel and Stravinsky, eagerly wrote pieces in which they tried to catch the spirit of "Le Blues." In the past thirty years the blues style has become so much of an international institution, so vital to music publishers, band leaders, Hollywood producers and radio directors that we are likely to forget how it all began and why.

When asked about the origin of the Blues some years ago, W. C. Handy, acknowledged "grandfather of the Blues," told Dorothy Scarborough:

"Most white people think that the Negro is always cheerful and lively, but he isn't, though he may seem that way when he is most troubled. The Negro knows the Blues as a state of mind, and that's why his music has that name.

"For instance, suppose I am a colored man, and my rent is due. It's twenty dollars, and my landlord has told me that if I don't pay him today he'll put me and my things out on the sidewalk. I haven't got the twenty dollars and I don't know where to get it. . . . I have scraped together ten dollars, but that's positively all I can get and that's not enough . . .

"Now when I know the time has come and I don't get that twenty dollars, what do I do? The white man would go to his landlord, offer him the ten, and maybe get the time extended. But what do I do? I go right out and blow that ten dollars I have and have a gay time. Anybody seeing me would think I was the jolliest darky in town, but it's just because I'm miserable and can't help myself.

"Now if the Negro were making a song about an experience like that, it would be a genuine specimen of Blues." *

Out of the miseries of the most despised class of Southern Negroes: nomadic laborers, street-corner gals, beggars, prisoners chain-gang-bound, came the first melancholy wail of the Blues. They were sung in Georgia, Mississippi, and Texas for at least ten or fifteen years before Handy first thought of writing them down. Said the celebrated Negro musician in 1925:

"Here's a thing called the 'Joe Turner Blues' . . . That is written around an old Negro song I used to hear and play thirty or more years ago. In some sections it was called 'Going Down the River for Long,' but in Tennessee it was always 'Joe Turner.' Joe Turner, the inspiration of the song, . . . was an officer and he used to come to Memphis and get prisoners to carry them to Nashville after a Kangaroo court. When the Negroes said of anyone, 'Joe Turner's been to town,' they

* Dorothy Scarborough: "On the Trail of Negro Folk Songs."

meant the person in question had been carried off handcuffed, to be gone no telling how long." *

Joe Turner had such wide currency all over the South that it has even been suggested that all the early Blues were sung to its tune, with the words being changed to fit the particular mood or situation of the person singing. The characteristic three-line form of the Blues was so simple that it was ideally suited to the constant addition or improvisation of new lyrics, one line being sung twice and then a third added to top them off:

Come wid his fo'ty links of chain— Oh Lawdy!
Come wid his fo'ty links of chain— Oh Lawdy!
Got my man, an' gone.

Thus the same tune—or at least the same musical pattern—could be used for the expression of any one of a dozen different emotions. The fact that the Blues were popularized and are still performed on the radio mainly by deep-throated female "hot" singers has led to the mistaken notion that they are always a woman's cry of longing for her "man." But, as Sterling Brown has pointed out, their subject matter is much broader than this, for there are Blues bemoaning "tornadoes, high water, hard times in farming, or insisting upon the need for travelling, for leaving this cold-hearted town. As well as self-pity, there is stoicism in the Blues." † Sarcastic indifference is not infrequently found, as in the following:

What you gwine to do when dey buhn de bar'l-
   house down?
What you gwine to do when dey buhn de bar'l-
   house down?
Gwine move out de piano, an' bar'l-house on de
   groun'.

When Handy, in 1912, published the first of his famous series, the "Memphis Blues" (which he had written three years before to help win the Memphis mayoralty election for one Mr. Crump) and sold it to a New York publisher for $100, it was the beginning of a new epoch for Tin Pan Alley. Blues were soon being written by the dozen, and recording companies, recognizing the potent appeal of the new type, began to send apparatus throughout the South to record folk Blues directly from the performance of illiterate rural Negro singers. Not only Memphis and St. Louis, but almost every state in the South and dozens of small towns had their special Blues, as the following list suggests:

Alabama Blues, Mississippi Blues, Lou'siana Low-down Blues, Virginia Blues, New Orleans Hop Scop Blues, Hampton Roads Blues, Shreveport Wiggle, Waco, Texas Blues, Georgia Hunch, New Orleans Wiggle, Selma Bama Blues,* and many others.

For the first time in history, perhaps, a folk style penetrated within a short time of its creation to the sophisticated centers of musical distribution, and was made known throughout the nation to a larger public than would ever have been possible through diffusion by normal methods. Such are the wonders of modern large-scale distribution.

The Blues, however, did not emerge unscathed from this process. The change in environment from the barrel-house, the prison cell, the riverside shack, whence the mournful songs had originally sprung, to the dance floors of elegant hotels or swanky metropolitan night clubs via the studio-suites of Broadway's highest paid arrangers produced a similar change in the physiognomy of the music itself. From the uncouth, rough-throated laments of a simple and unhappy people, they were turned into a languid, sophisticated, elegant entertainment and dance music, as silken as the gowns of the debutantes who danced to its strains on the roof-gardens of expensive hotels. The whole of the current controversy among the advocates of "hot" and "sweet" jazz hinges on the basic change that arose when the primitive folk blues got into the hands of the Tin Pan Alley arrangers. Working on salary for a market, they were more interested in turning out a slick, commercial product

---

* Scarborough: *Op. cit.*
† Sterling Brown: "Negro Poetry and Drama."

* We are indebted for this list to Odum and Johnson's "Negro Workaday Songs."

with a taste of "blue" quality, but shorn of all the roughness that might possibly irritate the ears of paying customers.

Although they both go by the same name, the primitive Blues and the sophisticated commercial product are two quite different kinds of music. As Abbe Niles has pointed out, the original Blues "were woven of the same stuff as . . . the work-songs, love songs, devil songs, the over-and-overs, slow drags, pats and stomps; yes, and decidedly the spirituals." * Winthrop Sargent in his "Jazz: Hot and Hybrid" has shown the essential identity between the musical style of the Negro rural congregations which produced the semi-barbaric "shoutin' spirituals" and that of authentic Blues singers like the late Bessie Smith. Common to both are the characteristic "Blue" intonations, the tendency to "worry" the third and seventh steps of the scale, the alternation between major and minor, the complete rhythmic freedom, the constant renewal of melodic and rhythmic patterns through invention and improvisation.

All these features were turned to account by Negro instrumentalists who played the "jazz" first in the dives of Memphis, New Orleans, and other Southern towns and then in the hotels and night clubs of metropolitan centers. When combined with a high development of instrumental virtuosity by both Negro and white performers, they led to the style that has been recently revived as "swing." In addition to forming the basis of this "hot" style, the Blues, when played as a slow juicy melody over a throbbing, pulsating background, harmonized by arrangers brought up on Puccini, Rimski-Korsakov and Debussy, form the core

* Abbe Niles: Introduction to Handy "Blues."

of that "sweet" style that is such an important segment of our popular music today.

In becoming a part of popular entertainment, the Blues acquired many traits of white European musical style not present in the primitive Negro variety. But even the folk variety itself was taken over and widely sung by rural white singers as well. Such are the Blues, "Chilly Winds," "Hungry Ragged Blues," and "Every Night When the Sun Goes In," recorded from the singing of white folk singers in the mountains, many of whom claimed to have composed the Blues themselves. Some of these do have a characteristic mountain quality, while still bearing traces of Negro origin. Thus we see in our own time and country how true music is no respecter of artificial boundaries, but can form a link of sympathy among all down-to-earth Americans.

Although we have discussed them at length, Blues and Jazz were not the only musical developments of the first decades of this century. There were others that reflected the dramatic events of the World War—the hundreds of popular songs ranging from "I Didn't Raise My Boy to Be a Soldier," "Joan of Arc," "Roses of Picardy," "Hello Central, Give Me No Man's Land," to more home-grown songs of the dough-boys, such as "Hinky Dinky" with its thousand and one verses that recorded every phase—including the unprintable—of Mr. John Q. American's experience "Over There." There were the songs of wandering hoboes and of the "wild boys" who rode the rods and camped in Hoovervilles looking for work. There were songs of the fat years and the lean, of riding on top of the world and of selling apples. This was the record of the comedy and tragedy, the joy, the hope, the human story of a growing, struggling, forward-moving America.

The Blues Ain' Nothin'

Arrangement
by Elie Siegmeister

Ah'm gon-na build mah- a raft An' float dat rib - bah down, ____ Ah'll build mah-self a shack In some ol' Tex-as town. 'Cause de blues am noth-in' No, de blues am noth-in' But a good man feel-in' blue. ____

DE BLUES AIN' NOTHIN'

MANY DISSERTATIONS have been written on the origin and meaning of folk song in general, jazz and the blues in particular. But perhaps the simplest and best explanation is that "De blues ain' nothin' but a good man feelin' blue."

This one was sung at an early date in honky-tonks in the Southwest.

2

Ah'm goin' down on de levee,
Goin' to take mahself a rockin' chair.
If mah lovin' man don' come,
Ah'll rock away from there.

CHORUS: 'Cause de, etc.

3

Why did you leave me blue?
Why did you leave me blue?
All ah do is sit
An' cry fo' you,

CHORUS: 'Cause de, etc.

Joe Turner Blues

Arrangement
by Elie Siegmeister

2

Dey tell me Joe Turner he done come
Dey tell me Joe Turner he done come
Come with fohty links of chain.

318

Joe Turney, brother of Pete Turney, who was Governor of Tennessee between 1892 and 1896, was in charge of bringing prisoners from Memphis to the Nashville penitentiary. His name (pronounced "Turner" by the Negroes) would bring the blue-est feelings to the sweethearts, mothers, wives of those he came after.

Abbe Niles tells us that "Joe Turner" was known throughout the South before there was any widespread singing of the folk-blues, and that it was sung to different words in various places. In Henderson, Kentucky, it was "Gwine down de river 'fo long." Down in Texas, strangely, it was "Michigan water tastes like sherry wine"; in the Sea Island cotton section of Georgia it was "Gwine down dat long, lonesome road."

"Joe Turner" has been called the grandfather of the Blues.

Friendless Blues

Words and Music
by W. C. Handy

Arrangement
by Elie Siegmeister

Feel so low- down an' sad Lawd,

Feel so low- down an' sad Lawd,

Lost ev - 'ry thing I ev-er had   Ain't got no

friend no - where   Lawd,   Ain't got no friend no -

where   Lawd,   All by my - self no one to care.

I met a man   in my own home town, in my   own home town

I met a man in my own home town,

Coaxed me a - way now he has thrown me down.

Mon-ey's all gone I'm so far from home, I'm so far from home

Mon-ey's all gone I'm so far from home far from home

I just sit here   all a-lone and cry an'   moan, cry an'   moan.

FRIENDLESS BLUES

AROUND 1890, Abbe Niles tells us, a guitar blues, "I Got No Mo' Home Den a Dog" was popular from Tennessee to Indiana. Handy in his "Blues" gives three different settings of this tune, ("Hearts and Flowers," "Tango" and "Charleston") which, he points out, represent the successive phases of its development at the hands of dance bands. Finally we come to Handy's own "Friendless Blues" (1926) version, which represents the latest stage. This includes the original twelve bars, dressed up in a more rhythmic accompaniment, and to which has been added an entirely new chorus, and new words. The whole constitutes a fascinating example of the transition from folk Blues to Broadway Blues.

2

I want to see that Indian River shore, Indian River shore
I want to see that Indian River shore,
If I get back I'll never leave no more.

3

When I was home the door was never closed, door was never closed
When I was home the door was never closed,
Where my home is now the good Lawd only knows.

4

'Member the time when I was young an' gay, when I was young an' gay
'Member the time when I was young an' gay,
Had many friends hanging 'round me ev'ry day.

Gambler's Blues
(St. James Infirmary Blues)

*Arrangement
by Elie Siegmeister*

It was down in old Joe's bar- -room On a cor-ner by the square, The drinks were served as us-ual, And a good-ly crowd was there. It was there.

2

On my left stood Joe McKenny,
His eyes bloodshot and red,
He gazed at the crowd around him
And these were the words he said:

THE GAMBLER'S (ST. JAMES INFIRMARY) BLUES

THE MILLIONAIRE GANGSTERS of the roaring twenties found that it was safe to exhibit their wealth only after they were dead. In Chicago, silver coffins were the sign of elegance among the racketeers' elite.

This classic blues starts with drink and a broken heart, and winds up in a grandiose finale. The gambler's vision of his resplendent funeral with its sixteen coal-black horses, its crap-shooting pall-bearers, its hell-raising jazz band, could serve as a model for short-futured gunmen.

3

"As I passed by the old infirmary,
I saw my sweetheart there,
All stretched out on a table,
So pale, so cold, so fair.

4

Went up to see the doctor,
'She's very low,' he said:
Went back to see my woman,
Good God! She's layin' there dead,
Spoken: She's dead!

5

Sixteen coal-black horses,
All hitched to a rubber-tired hack,
Carried seven girls to the graveyard,
And only six of 'em comin' back.

6

O, when I die, just bury me
In a box-back coat and hat,
Put a twenty dollar gold piece on my watch chain
To let the Lord know I'm standing pat.

7

Six crap shooters as pall bearers,
Let a chorus girl sing me a song
With a jazz band on my hearse
To raise hell as we go along.

8

And now you've heard my story,
I'll take another shot of booze;
If anybody happens to ask you,
Then I've got those gambler's blues."

Po' Boy

Arrangement
by Elie Siegmeister

326

Run a - way with an - oth - er man, po' boy, Run a - way with an -

oth - er man. I got to think - in' a - bout the

wo - man I love, She run a - way with an - oth - er man, po' boy!

2

As I went down to the big depot,
The train came a-rumblin' by.
I looked in the window, saw the woman I loved,
And I hung my head and cried.

I hung my head and cried, po' boy,
I hung my head and cried.
I looked in the window, saw the woman I loved,
And I hung my head and cried.

PO' BOY

THE CONVICT who first moaned out this "penitentiary-bound" Blues had certainly never read the definition which tells us that "the blues have a twelve bar melody, in three phrases, with 'breaks' between them, and a strong tendency towards the subdominant throughout." Po' boy! His lament scarcely fills this bill; but withal, it is one of the most indigo of Blues. "Po' Boy" is also known under the title, "The Coon-can Game."

3

I jumped right on the train platform,
I walked right down the aisle.
I pulled out my forty-some odd
And I shot that dark-skinned child.

I shot that dark-skinned child, po' boy,
I shot that dark-skinned child.
I pulled out my forty-some odd
And I shot that dark-skinned child.

4

They took me down to the big court house;
The judge he looked at me.
I said, "Oh, kind-hearted Judge,
What am it gwine to be?"

What am it gwine to be, po' boy,
What am it gwine to be?
I say, "Oh, kind-hearted Judge,
What am it gwine to be?"

5

The judge he heard the contract read,
The clerk, he took it down.
They handed me over to the contractor,
And now I'm penitentiary-bound.

And now I'm penitentiary-bound, po' boy,
And now I'm penitentiary-bound.
They handed me over to the contractor,
And now I'm penitentiary-bound.

6

The night was cold and stormy,
It sho' did look like rain.
I ain't got a friend in the whole wide world,
Nobody knows my name.

Nobody knows my name, po' boy,
Nobody knows my name.
I ain't got a friend in the whole wide world,
Nobody knows my name.

Every Night When the Sun Goes In

*Arrangement
by Elie Siegmeister*

I wish to the Lord my babe was born,
A-sitting upon his papa's knee,
And me, poor girl, was dead and gone,
And the green grass growing over me.

CHORUS: True love, *etc.*

ALTHOUGH HAVING neither the rhythm nor the form of the conventional
Blues, this mountain lament has in it so much of bleakness and desolation that its "blue" mood would be hard to match.

Hallejuah, I'm a Bum

*Arrangement
by Elie Siegmeister*

HALLELUJAH, I'M A BUM

HARVEST HANDS who follow the sun and the crops around the seasons often find themselves "riding the rods" and wondering where the next job is going to turn up. Also there minds often center around that engaging question: when does the next meal come along? This song was a familiar one, sung outside the doors of Salvation Army missions for many years.

2

Oh, I love my boss and my boss loves me,
And that is the reason that I'm so hungry.

CHORUS: Hallelujah, I'm a bum, etc.

3

Oh, springtime has come; I'm just out of jail,
Without any money, without any bail.

CHORUS: Hallelujah, I'm a bum, etc.

4

I went to a house and I knocked on the door;
A lady came out, says, "You've been here before."

CHORUS: Hallelujah, I'm a bum, etc.

5

I went to a house and I asked for some bread;
A lady came out, says, "The baker is dead."

CHORUS: Hallelujah, I'm a bum, etc.

6

When springtime does come, oh, won't we have fun
We'll throw up our jobs and we'll go on the bum.

CHORUS: Hallelujah, I'm a bum, etc.

The Preacher and the Slave

Words by Joe Hill
Tune of "In the Sweet Bye and Bye"

Arrangement
by Elie Siegmeister

Long-haired preach - ers come out ev' - ry night; And they tell you what's wrong and what's right; But when asked a - bout some - thing to eat, They will an - swer with voi - ces so sweet:

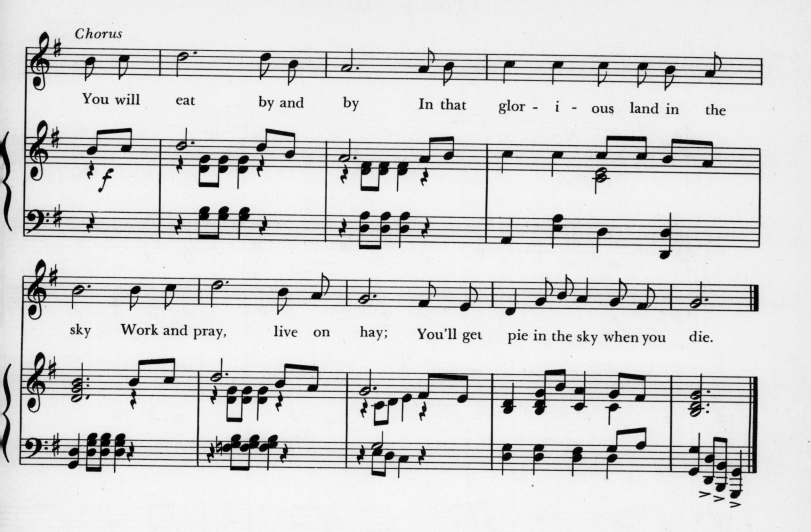

Chorus

You will eat by and by In that glor - i - ous land in the sky Work and pray, live on hay; You'll get pie in the sky when you die.

THE PREACHER AND THE SLAVE

WHEN JOE HILL was executed in Utah in 1915, men on the road, in jungles, in jails, and in union halls from California to Alabama to Massachusetts mourned his passing, for his songs were known and sung far and wide. On the eve of his death, he wrote:

My will is easy to decide,
For there is nothing to divide

Till I Find My Den

Arrangement
by Elie Siegmeister

Moderately, Very Sustained

Till ah fin' mah den   Ahm go in' up de riv - er,

Till ah fin' mah den   Ahm gon- na leave you here.

Sez ah been down   on de bum so long

Till ah lose de use of mah right arm.

334

Hinky Dinky

Arrangement
by Elie Siegmeister

Oh far - mer have you a daught - er fair, par — lay- voo, Oh

far - mer have you a daught - er fair, par — lay- voo, Oh

far - mer have you a daught - er fair Who can wash a sold - ier's

un - der - wear? Hin - ky din - ky par - lay- voo.

HINKY DINKY

EVERY WAR starts with its quota of energetic, rousing songs. They are played by bands with shiny new instruments and printed in neat song books.

When the soldier boys get through with them, they sometimes turn out quite differently. "Hinky Dinky" records the adventures of Bud, Mac and Jim "somewhere in France." It was the favorite of the A.E.F., and there were dozens of verses giving the "off-the-record" thoughts and doings of the dough boys.

2

Mademoiselle from Armentières, parlay-voo,
Mademoiselle from Armentières, parlay-voo,
Mademoiselle from Armentières,
She never heard of underwear.
Hinky dinky parlay-voo.

3

The captain's carrying the pack, parlay-voo,
The captain's carrying the pack, parlay-voo,
The captain's carrying the pack
I hope to God it breaks his back.
Hinky dinky parlay-voo.

4

The officers get all the steak, parlay-voo,
The officers get all the steak, parlay-voo,
The officers get all the steak
And all we get is a belly-ache.
Hinky dinky parlay-voo.

5

One night I had "beaucoup" jack, parlay-voo,
One night I had "beaucoup" jack, parlay-voo,
One night I had "beaucoup" jack
Till a Mademoiselle got on my track.
Hinky dinky parlay-voo.

6

The M.P.'s say they won the war, parlay-voo,
The M.P.'s say they won the war, parlay-voo,
The M.P.'s say they won the war
Standing guard at a cafe door.
Hinky dinky parlay-voo.

7

The general got the croix-de-guerre, parlay-voo,
The general got the croix-de-guerre, parlay-voo,
The general got the croix-de-guerre
The son-of-a-gun never was there.
Hinky dinky parlay-voo.

8

The generals stayed behind the line, parlay-voo,
The generals stayed behind the line, parlay-voo,
The generals stayed behind the line
With plenty of women and plenty of wine.
Hinky dinky parlay-voo.

9

From gay Paree we heard guns roar, parlay-voo,
From gay Paree we heard guns roar, parlay-voo,
From gay Paree we heard guns roar,
But all that we learned was "Je t'adore."
Hinky dinky parlay-voo.

10

They say it is a terrible war, parlay-voo,
They say it is a terrible war, parlay-voo,
They say it is a terrible war
But what the hell are we fighting it for?
Hinky dinky parlay-voo.

16. Broadway to Route 66

AFTER MORE than two hundred years of development, American song is still in the making. Unlike the popular and folk songs of certain other lands whose creative well-springs seem to have gone dry, our songs have come up abundantly as cucumbers in rich soil. This music of today is not full of yearning for the archaic, the faraway, the unobtainable; instead, it reflects the life of today; not only the America of romance, day-dreams, boy-meets-girl, but also the land of railroads, airplanes, great roads and dams, dust bowls, people on the move. From Broadway to Route 66 (the road on which the Joads travelled to the Promised Land) there is a nation singing, singing songs bitter and sweet, lovely and harsh—but singing.

With the triumph of the radio and the sound film, the distinction between the music of the city and the country has grown smaller. The old traditions of native country music have been drowned out by the roar of the loud speaker. The music of Broadway and Hollywood has penetrated to the lonely mountain valley, to the horseman on the plains, to the lumberjack deep in the woods. The handiwork of the obscure Negro in the South comes back to him, modified, clothed in elegant costume, amplified a thousand-fold.

Jazz, which is so commonplace a part of our daily lives that we eat, breathe, dance, work, ride, go to sleep with it, is music with many faces. To some critics, it is our country's greatest contribution to music; to the high-brows, an annoyance; to the jitterbugs and swing fanatics, an ecstatic ritual; to the big publishers and booking agents, a vastly profitable industry; to the average boy and girl, something to dance to.

As a term, jazz has been used to describe many more different types of music than any other word in the dictionary. It has been applied to old-time rag-time tunes brought up to date; to Tyrolean and Neapolitan folk songs, and to melodies from Tschaikovsky, Chopin, Debussy, recast into popular vein; to simple ditties written for Disney cartoons and to stepped-up symphonic essays played by our leading orchestras. Some maintain that jazz is not the music played, but the manner of playing it, while others hold that true jazz is to be found not in the products of Tin Pan Alley, or issuing from the silver trumpets of top name orchestras, but rather from the unpublicized scrapes and tootlings of obscure ensembles of broken-down old-timers in some gin mill at three in the morning.

As the fads come and go, the many different things called Jazz remain and develop. No one school has a monopoly on the vitality behind it all. Certainly the would-be barbarians who revel in the mysteries of boogie woogie and jive have energy, rhythm and excitement on their side. But possibly more lasting are the popular songs of a Handy, a Gershwin, a Jerome Kern. Certainly "The St. Louis Blues," "Summertime," and "Old Man River" will live on, possibly because of the strong folk elements they contain. What matter if they are not "pure"—if they are hybrids of "hot" and "sweet," of African rhythms and European harmonic subtleties? The result is uniquely and distinctively American.

Some have pointed to the short life of the average Tin Pan Alley song as proof of the ephemeral nature of jazz. Of the approximately 10,000 songs published yearly up to a short time ago, certainly few still live on to trouble us. Radio has cut the life span of the successful tune from the former one or two years to a matter of three or four months, at the most. Most jazz songs are short-lived. Since they seek only surface entertainment values, they are unable to take root in deep human feelings. Folk songs, on the other hand, possess a universal character and deal with basic experiences.

There are a few tunes that become "semi-classics." In addition to those already mentioned, one might include "Dinah," "Night and Day," and "Stardust." Possibly these will occupy the position in the future that "Kiss Me Again," "Let Me Call You Sweetheart," and "Sidewalks of New York" hold today. Many popular songs of former years have been taken over by the people and made into folk songs: "Barbara Allen," "Bury Me Not on the Lone Prairie," "Sweet Betsy From Pike," and possibly the same thing may happen with some of our current popular songs. Perhaps some of them may attain the place occupied today by the tunes of a Tin Pan Alley composer of an earlier year: Stephen Foster.

Whatever its future, jazz has entered the body of serious music as well. It has touched the songs of Charles Ives, the orchestral works of Morton Gould, the theatrical music of Marc Blitzstein.

While Hollywood, the radio, and Tin Pan Alley have overshadowed the unsophisticated rural music of this country, this music has by no means vanished. Far from Broadway, in the sand-dunes of Florida, the coal country of Harlan, Ky., in the dust-bowl of Oklahoma, the traditions of "ballad-makin' " are alive and vigorous as ever. The phonograph has recently brought to light again the fact that out in the "barren hinterland" of America, the old earthy music is still flourishing. Not as pretty, not as sweet, not as flashy as that of Tin Pan Alley; no tricky orchestrations, no swooning crooners; no musical stunts. But the body and bone of America are still there. The voice of the mountain still sharp and angular, the spiritual still full-throated, the prairie lullaby soft and tender. And news: of storms, tornadoes, big things coming up; highways, dams, the TVA; escapes from the chain gang; migrations from the dusty country. A people on the move, a march of the Israelites out of Egypt on Route 66. We have read of it in Steinbeck's book, seen it in John Ford's movie; and now we hear it from the guitar of the "dustiest of the dust-bowlers, Woody Guthrie. Another rusty-voiced Homer, he sings the story of the "Grapes of Wrath" because "the Okies back there haven't got two bucks to buy the book, or even thirty-five cents to see the movie, but the song will get back to them and tell them what Preacher Casey Casey said."

Right out of the heart of America, out of to-day it comes, to remind us

Our country's strong, our country's young,
*And her greatest songs are still unsung.**

* John La Touche in the "Ballad for Americans."

O Lord

*Arrangement
by Elie Siegmeister*

Oh, boss man, tell me, What have you done? How come you lock me a-way From de light of de sun, O Lord!

A TERRIFYING SONG from a Georgia chain gang, recorded in 1938.

2

No standin' place here,
No set, no lay me down;
Double iron shackles
From my head on down to de groun'.

3

Locked in mah coffin
Long befo' mah time,
Great God a-mercy,
Ain' commit no hangin' crime.

4

Jerge gi' me short sentence,
Twenty days and fine,
Ain't heard 'em say nothin'
'Bout no buryin' me alive.

5

Please, cool kin' Cap'n,
Drink o' water 'fo' I choke.
He say go ast old debbil
Hell's fire you're gonna stoke.

By permission of Lawrence Gellert, from *Me and My Captain,* copyright 1939
by Hours Press

Sistern and Brethern

*Arrangement
by Elie Siegmeister*

Slowly Majestic

Sis-tern and breth-ren, stop fool-in' wid pray, Sis-tern and breth-ren,

stop fool-in' wid pray, When black face is lift-ed, Lawd turn-in' way.

WALLINGFORD RIEGGER felt that this song "may, in time, take a place
beside "Go Down, Moses." Be that as it may, it is evidence of the fact
that the South is still producing noble and heart-stirring folk music.

We're buryin' a brudder dey kill for de crime,
We're buryin' a brudder dey kill for de crime,
Tryin' to keep what was his all de time.

When we's tucked him on under what you goin' to do?
When we's tucked him on under what you goin' to do?
Wait till dey arousin' fo' you?

I'm Goin' Down This Road Feeling Bad

Words and Music
by Woody Guthrie

Arrangement
by Elie Siegmeister

I'm a-goin' down this road a-feel-in' bad, I'm a-goin' down this road a-feel-in' bad, I'm a-goin' down this road a-feel-in' bad, yes Lord, And I ain't a-gon-na be treat-ed this a-way.

GOIN' DOWN THIS ROAD FEELIN' BAD

WOODY GUTHRIE, one of the many Okie balladeers who sing this song tells us: "I don't know nothing about music. Never could read or write it. But somehow or other, when the black old dust hit our country, I was among the first to blow. When it cleared off again, I woke up with a guitar in one hand and a road map in the other one. Went as far as the map said, and the cops said it was California."

A song that is well-known along U. S. Route 66, it was sung by the character, Eddie, in the motion picture of "Grapes of Wrath."

2

Yes, they fed me on cornbread and beans,
Yes, they fed me on cornbread and beans,
They fed me on cornbread and beans, yes Lord,
And I ain't a-gonna be treated this a-way.

3

Got me way down in jail on my knees,
Got me way down in jail on my knees,
Got me way down in jail on my knees, yes Lord,
And I ain't a-gonna be treated this a-way.

4

Takes a ten dollah shoe to fit my feet,
Takes a ten dollah shoe to fit my feet,
Takes a ten dollah shoe to fit my feet, yes Lord,
And I ain't a-gonna be treated this a-way.

5

I'm a-goin' down where the climate suits my clothes,
I'm a-goin' down where the climate suits my clothes,
I'm a-goin' down where the climate suits my clothes,
And I ain't a-gonna be treated this a-way.

Tom Joad

Words and Music
by Woody Guthrie

Arrangement
by Elie Siegmeister

Lively Guitar style

Tom Joad got out of the old Mc Al - est - er Pen And

there he got his Pa - role; Aft - er four long years on a

man- kill - in' charge, Tom Joad came a-walk - in' down the road, poor boy, Tom

1st and others   *last*

Joad came a-walk - in' down the road.

TOM JOAD

FEW COULD TELL the story of "Grapes of Wrath" more compactly and with greater force than the simple ballad, "Tom Joad" by Woody Guthrie.

2

Tom Joad he caught a truck-driving man
And there he caught him a ride;
He said, "I just got out of McAlester Pen
On a charge called 'Homicide'—poor boy,
On a charge called 'Homicide.'"

3

That truck rolled away in a big cloud of dust,
Tommy turned his face toward home,
He met Preacher Casey and they had a little drink
But he found that his family they had gone, Tom
He found that his family they had gone.

4

He found his mother's old fashioned shoe,
He found his daddy's hat,
He found little Muley, and little Muley said,
"They been tractored out by Cats, Tom,
They been tractored out by Cats."

5

The twelve of the Joads made a mighty heavy load,
And Grandpa Joad did cry,
As he took up a handful of land in his hand,
Said, "I'm stickin' with the farm till I die!
I'm stickin' with the farm till I die."

6

Tom Joad went down to the Neighbor's farm,
There he found his Family;
They packed their duds, and loaded in a car,
His mother said, "We got to git away, Tom,"
His mother said, "We got to git away."

7

They fed him shortribs, coffee, and soothing syrup,
And Grandpa Joad did die—
They buried Grandpa Joad by the side of the road;
Grandma on the California side,
Grandma on the California side.

8

They stood on a mountain and they looked toward the West
And it looked like the Promised Land,
A bright green valley with a river running through,
There was work for every single hand, they thought,
There was work for every single hand.

The Joads rolled into a Jungle Camp,
And there Ma cooked a stew,
And the hungry little kids of the Jungle Camp
Said, "We'd like to have some, too, Miss,
We'd like to have some, too."

A Deputy Sheriff cut loose at a man,
He shot a woman in the back;
Before he could take his aim again,
It was Preacher Casey dropped him in his tracks, Boy,
Preacher Casey dropped him in his tracks.

They handcuffed Casey and they took him to jail,
And then he got away,
He met Tom Joad by the old River Bridge,
And these few words he did say, Preacher Casey,
It was these few words he did say:

The Deputies come, and Tom and Casey run
To a place where the water run down;
There a Vigilante thug hit Casey with a club,
And he laid Preacher Casey on the ground, Boy,
He laid Preacher Casey on the ground.

"Well, I preached for the Lord for a mighty long time,
I preached about the rich and the poor;
Us workin' folks has got to get together,
'Cause we ain't got a chance anymore, Boys,
We ain't got a chance anymore."

14

Tom Joad he grabbed that Deputy's club,
He brought it down on his head,
Tom Joad took flight in that dark, rainy night,
A Deputy and a Preacher layin' dead, two men,
A Deputy and a Preacher layin' dead.

15

Tom Joad ran back to where his Mother was asleep,
He woke her up out of bed,
He kissed "goodbye" to the mother that he loved,
And he said what Preacher Casey said, Tom Joad,
He said what Preacher Casey said:

16

"Everybody must be just One Big Soul
It looks that way to me;
Wherever you look in the day or night,
That's where I'm a goin' to be, Ma,
That's where I'm goin' to be.

17

Wherever Little Children are hungry and cry,
Wherever people ain't free—
Wherever men are a-fightin' for their rights,
That's where I'm a-goin' to be, Ma,
That's where I'm a-goin' to be."

The following songs represented in this book have been recorded by the American Ballad Singers, directed by Elie Siegmeister, and are included in Victor Album P-41:

"Poor Wayfaring Stranger"
"Springfield Mountain"
"Go to Sleepy"
"Kentucky Moonshiner"

Index of Song Titles